Autobiographical Tales

Autobiographical Tales

Peter Keating

Priskus
Edinburgh

© Peter Keating, 2013

Published by Priskus Books, Edinburgh.
Email pjk@priskusbooks.co.uk

A CIP catalogue record for this book is available from the British Library.

ISBN 978-0-9926507-0-4

Book and cover design by Clare Brayshaw

'Silver Trumpet', painting by Ruth Addinall
Photographs by Valerie Shaw and Peter Keating.

Prepared and printed by:

York Publishing Services Ltd
64 Hallfield Road
Layerthorpe
York YO31 7ZQ

Tel: 01904 431213

Website: www.yps-publishing.co.uk

Contents

Introduction

In the early days of psychoanalysis Sigmund Freud liked to point out how 'strange' it was that although he was qualified as a medical doctor and trained in various scientific procedures, the case histories he wrote 'read like short stories.' He was afraid that it might lead to his work being seen as lacking 'the serious stamp of science.' It's difficult to know whether Freud was genuinely worried by this possibility. There was no good reason why he should have been. He had a great love of imaginative literature and always acknowledged the profound influence that poets and dramatists had on his work. He also frequently observed that while psychoanalysis dealt centrally with the same basic human emotions, feelings and experiences as imaginative literature, they were generally ignored by medicine and science.

Even so, Freud's concern at the problems caused by crossing intellectual and imaginative boundaries was understandable. It meant challenging the natural possessiveness of specialists and drawing upon himself the accusation of intervening in matters that were properly speaking none of his business. The uncertainties raised about the exact nature of Freud's work persist, now as then. Were the claims he was making for psychoanalysis scientific or not? What kind of doctor diagnosed illnesses that had no obvious physical symptoms? Should he be regarded as a medical or scientific man at all, or was he simply imagining things, making them up? As his case studies truly do read like short stories of a particularly adventurous and absorbing kind, shouldn't we simply accept him as a writer or artist?

In all of this, as in so many other ways, Freud was anticipating a preoccupation of many twentieth-century writers who have resented having their work placed too easily and misleadingly into rigid categories. Until the middle of the 1990s I would have described my own writing as literary history of a distinct interdisciplinary nature. Its focal point was imaginative literature explored within a detailed social context, and this took in a number of other areas of study, notably history, economics, and politics. It did not, though, have any immediate connections with science or psychoanalysis. Nor, it would usually have been assumed, could it have anything at all to do with 'imaginative' or 'creative' writing, the most jealously and narrowly guarded of all types of literary classification.

Yet those meditations of Freud's affected me in a very special way. The more I considered them, the more they came to mean to me. Not that in writing *Autobiographical Tales* I had been looking to imitate Freud. No doubt my admiration for his work is apparent in many different ways in the present book, but I was consciously aware of it as operating most directly upon me in one very specific instance. It is not too much to say that without Freud's wry comments on the peculiar mixture of fiction and scientific probity in his early case studies, *Autobiographical Tales* would probably never have been written, and most certainly not in its present form.

In chronological terms, *Autobiographical Tales* ends in 1990, the year I took early retirement from the University of Edinburgh where for some two decades I had taught English literature and written literary history. I had a clear purpose in wanting to retire from full-time work at the age of fifty, but before taking that up there was some unfinished academic work to be done. For a long time I had hoped to argue the case for Rudyard Kipling as being an unjustly neglected poet, and it was this task I set myself in the first years of my retirement. It resulted in two closely related books: a biographical study published by Secker and Warburg and a Penguin anthology of Kipling's poetry, or 'verse' as he himself always called it. *Kipling the Poet* drew attention to the very special role played by poetry in Kipling's life. *Rudyard Kipling: Selected Poems,* though only the latest of many such selections from Kipling's poetry was substantially different from its predecessors in being edited according to firm scholarly principles. It was now possible to establish for the first time a reliable chronology of Kipling's poems, allowing them to be read not randomly, as they tended to be, but in the order in which they had been published.

Introduction

With this work completed I was able to turn to the ambition that had preoccupied me for even longer than the Kipling project. For as many years as I could remember I had wanted to write fiction and had always expected that one day I would do so. The attempts I had made at various times in my life amounted to nothing sustained or substantial, and I knew that that situation was not going to be changed by casual effort or wishful thinking. It had to be a purposeful, focused effort. So, I decided that the Kipling books would be my last works of literary history, and that I would also give up reviewing books, something I had done on a regular basis for many years, mainly for the *TLS* and the *Financial Times*. With these various obstacles – university, full-time paid work, literary history, book reviewing – out of the way, I could concentrate entirely on writing fiction.

I say 'writing fiction' as though it was something I was able to switch on much as I had decided to switch off literary history, though it didn't feel like that. It's true that for most of my life I had been a keen reader of fiction. I had studied it, lectured on it and written about it as well. Even so, I didn't make the mistake of believing that because I knew a lot about fiction it would be easy to write it. It did matter, though whether positively or negatively I have never been entirely sure, that I wasn't driven by having the idea of a particular novel on my mind. It was fiction as such that I wanted to see if I could handle and I began by experimenting with some of its component parts: dialogue, description, atmosphere, reliable and unreliable narrators, dramatic scenes or whatever. If these starting points looked as though they might develop into a novel I then followed them through. I was already sufficiently experienced as a writer to know that what I had set myself would be difficult, and I vowed that if after a while I couldn't produce something that wasn't to my mind of a high enough standard then I would give up on the attempt.

Crazy as it now seems, I at first allowed myself only six months of concentrated effort to learn whether or not I was likely to succeed. I don't mean that I expected to produce anything significant in this time. But I did think it would be long enough for me to discover whether it was worth my while continuing. That expectation was entirely unrealistic. The writing itself proved so fascinating and so addictive that the six months were extended to a year, then another year, and so on. After a period of some four or five years I had experimented with, and in the main completed, a campus novel, a metaphysical thriller, a documentary or sociological novel about suburban life, and a postmodernist novella centred on a group of poker players.

The enjoyment of carrying out these experiments didn't blunt my understanding that the standards I had set for myself weren't being met. The fiction I was writing seemed to me to be interesting enough, in some respects a bit more than simply that, but ultimately lacking the freshness and spontaneity I would have liked to find in it. The responses of publishers and literary agents who were approached largely confirmed my own judgments. According to the original plan I should now have faced the fact that I had made a wrong decision, console myself with the knowledge that the attempt in itself had been well worth making, and abandon the whole project. But it turned out that retreat wasn't necessary because I was slowly coming to understand what was wrong.

In putting literary history so firmly behind me in favour of fiction, I had not only been trying to ignore a style of writing that had taken me years of hard work to develop, but with it techniques and approaches that had also become second nature to me. Instead of allowing itself to be discarded in favour of new and untried ways of writing, the interdisciplinary method was proving resistant to change, even perhaps impossible to disentangle. The reason why my novels were in the final instance unconvincing was that they were sounding less and less like fiction as normally understood and more and more like fictionalized social history. I was in something of the dilemma that Freud had described so memorably when he found himself engaged in what he thought was one kind of writing only to discover that it read like something else.

Freud's response had not been to shut off the techniques of fiction that were deeply rooted in his own imagination, but to continue using them in order to communicate as forcefully as possible the new 'scientific' principles of psychoanalysis. It made good sense for me to take a similarly positive approach, albeit in a rather different direction. If my imagination was insisting that it felt more natural for it to continue examining social and political issues and didn't want to be wrenched in another direction, then wouldn't it be a good idea to follow its lead and try to apply the lessons I had learned from my interdisciplinary studies to the writing of fiction? In other words, positively extend and expand the interdisciplinary approach rather than artificially reject it. As with literary history, the mix would consist of whichever subject I felt it necessary to follow up at any particular point in the narrative, except that it would now include a cohesive element of fiction.

It was particularly helpful to me at this time to recognize that in the exercises I had set for myself at the very beginning I usually preferred writing from the point of view of a first-person rather than a third-person narrator. No doubt this was because it allowed me to comment, whether in my own or an adopted voice, on the subject being explored, as I was used to doing in non-fictional writing. It's even possible that this preference was in itself an indication that subconsciously I had not been entirely at ease in trying to work within the conventional forms of fiction. It was certainly only when I saw the narrative advantages of introducing autobiography as a controlling element in a new kind of interdisciplinary blend, that something of the shape of what I wanted to create began to emerge.

Each of the three memoirs that make up *Autobiographical Tales* is set in a different decade of the twentieth century and each of them deals with a distinct phase of my life. 'Kenny' takes place in the 1950s and early 1960s; 'Monica' very precisely in the years from 1968 to 1972; and 'Trevor' in the 1980s. They do not claim in any way to offer a full account of personal experiences. In fact, they deliberately exclude much that one would normally expect to find in a more conventional autobiography. There is nothing, for instance, about personal or intimate relationships and little about people met or known (celebrated or otherwise). These kinds of absence might justifiably be described as part of the book's fictional element in that key events are often described as taking place within an atmosphere of isolation that would be very unlikely to apply in a purely autobiographical context. But it can also be claimed, and with equal justice, that these are not really omissions at all but necessary choices made by me to create a consistent image of the autobiographical narrator/novelist of the 'tales.'

The first of those choices was to focus each of the tales on a relationship with someone who had been especially important to me at a particular moment of time. Once again, these relationships are very far from being close or intimate. In fact, I myself was not fully aware of how distanced I had made them until the book was almost completed. Kenny, Monica and Trevor all emerge, I hope, with personalities of their own, even if they are allowed to express themselves only through their interplay with me, their narrator and biographer. But distanced they now are, so much so in Monica's case that the truly central figure of the tale is perhaps not really Monica at all. Instead, that role is usurped by the mysterious, brooding, pervasive presence who was always hovering behind Monica and who would eventually enable me to interpret the cipher that I found her to be. In contrast, Kenny was both a fellow enthusiast and a counterbalance to my own views and attitudes. Here he allows me to return to the formative passions, prejudices and experiences of my adolescent years. Many years on, Trevor forced me to look not only into myself but also more closely at what was going on around me, challenging the state of isolation I had run into, and in a sense actively sought, that is a developing theme throughout the book.

And, of course, *Autobiographical Tales* also aims to explore my own experiences and those of my three protagonists in terms of very specific social moments. 'Kenny' is about what it was like to be a part of the jazz revivalist movement in Britain during the years following on from the end of the Second World War. Any part I myself played in all of this was, I'm perfectly happy to admit, very small, but in many ways it was a representative one as well, and that is how I have tried to present it here. 'Monica' examines what becoming a university lecturer meant to me in the late 1960s and how it influenced, determined even, my life for many years to come. 'Trevor' picks up on that strand of the story, exploring the nature of academic life in the 1980s, the political upheaval that changed Britain so decisively, and the spectacular rise and collapse of the modern British university system.

In all of these tales I have wanted particularly to convey a true and detailed impression of life as I have lived and experienced it. I felt that this could be best achieved for me, autobiographically as it were, through the various career, aesthetic and intellectual activities that have meant so much to me – playing the trumpet, writing, jazz, books, politics (at moments of both enthusiasm and disillusion), the life-long fascination with both literature and history and an ingrained curiosity about the ways in which the present has been moulded by the past. And always, the drive to find ways of shaping these various experiences and communicating their significance to others. Underlying everything is the influence my working-class childhood and upbringing has had upon virtually every aspect of my later life.

When I first began writing *Autobiographical Tales* I sent a memo to myself saying that the tales were to be written in such a way that they could be read either as autobiography or social history or fiction, or as a blend of all three. That message remains unchanged. In the few instances where I have deliberately introduced people under their own names, I must, of course, take responsibility for what I say about them. Anyone who is not identifiable in this way should be regarded as either a representative type or an invention. The same applies to events as well as people.

As this book has taken some years to write, and as the period of time it covers stretches back even further, the personal debts I have incurred are of an unusually wide-ranging kind, though my gratitude is no less on that count. I wish to dedicate 'Kenny' to the memory of my brother Harry (1933-2012) and to my sister Jennifer Moss; 'Monica' to Jim Stacey; and 'Trevor' to Valerie Shaw.

Peter Keating
March 2013

Kenny

'It's certainly funny to hear those youngsters trying to play like old men.' Bobby Hackett.

Hear Me Talkin' To Ya. Edited by Nat Shapiro and Nat Hentoff (1955)

I can remember the place itself without any trouble at all. There's no need for me to search through documentary records, stir up a failing memory, rely on wayward epiphanies or spend much effort of any kind to find my way back to this particular fragment of my past. All I have to do is think of it – or *want* to think of it, because wanting seems to be the only active effort involved – and there it is, instantly present. Picture-like, certainly, though not simply a picture. Far more than that. A complete physical presence. Shape, appearance, setting, atmosphere, social ambience and, most of all, because this story is mainly about the different sounds that were produced inside the place, its extraordinary acoustics.

As the times I'm talking about were totally absorbing and trouble free there would seem to be every reason for them to rest contentedly in my memory, all set to appear whenever summoned. And that, in the main, is how they are. Except for the ease of recall. That's what bothers me. I can't help thinking that some degree of mental effort would be appropriate. It feels as though without it my memory may be playing me false. I hope it isn't, but that's how it feels. Something crucial is missing, and I don't know what. It's not simply a matter of completing the general picture by filling in a few missing details, or even of clarifying a couple of fuzzy recollections. There's some kind of separation involved, as though a key section of the experience has detached itself and slid away from the rest.

It's the place itself, as I have said, that I have no problem remembering. What worries me is that I can't describe how to get to it. I don't mean *now* as though it has become some dilapidated heritage site kept unreasonably boarded up and away from public gaze, a place that tourists would love to visit if they were only allowed the chance. Nothing like that! In fact I'd be amazed if it's still standing after all these years. And even if it is, there's no chance of a commemorative blue plaque being attached to its shabby walls. What I mean is that I couldn't give details *now* of how I used to get to it *then*. Unambiguous street directions are out of the question. Turn left by The Spotted Cow, walk straight ahead for about five hundred yards, take the second on the right and there you are. That kind of thing.

In my time I must have acted out such directions over and over again, instinctively, unthinkingly. Now they're gone, and I'm sure that if put to the test I wouldn't be able to find my own way there let alone direct someone else. The first half of the journey, the easy mechanical bit, is straightforward. But after that the memory gives up. 'That's enough,' it announces, in the manner of an old-style bus conductor. 'No more. Your ticket doesn't take you any further. This is your stop.' So I get off the bus, and then, left to my own devices, I've nothing to contribute, no way of moving forward.

I've tried often enough, but all that comes to mind is an impenetrable maze of streets, like one of those woods in folktales and romances where the trees grow so densely together that even the rays of the sun are unable to provide the young hero with any helpful light. Until, that is, the very moment when he is due to arrive at his fated destination. Then, on the verge of surrendering the quest in despair, he is certain to find – seductively comfortable and nonsensically settled in a sun-bathed glade at the very heart of the wood – a castle or tower or sweet little cottage.

That's how it feels to me, though the building at the heart of my suburban forest was neither romantic nor pretty, and it most certainly wasn't sweet. I don't think it even had a proper name to be remembered or forgotten by. We called it 'The Centre.' It was a squat many-sided building, octagonal probably, but so misshapen that it could have had any number of sides, occupying a large square patch of ground that I suspect might once have been a village green. Now, though, there was very little grass or space around it. The Centre took up the whole area. It was set on a concrete base which at various points could be seen jutting out from underneath. There was a short gravel path leading to a heavy wooden front door, but no fence, wall, or any formal boundary at all. Serving this purpose was a narrow strip of pavement that ran all the way round the building. Beyond that, and running parallel to it, there was a rather smart tarmacked road, ringed by another much broader pavement, and then dozens of scrupulously neat detached and semi-detached villas, all with short front gardens, the entrances to which created a decorative fringe of wooden gates and privet hedges.

At two of the square's corners there were exits and entrances to and from the larger world. These were used constantly by whoever lived in the houses and also by visitors to the Centre. Round and about, in and out they went, the residents and the visitors, never meeting up with each other. The whole scene might have been compared imaginatively to a small medieval moated castle, its inner-directed community resolutely intent on pursuing its own interests yet still near enough to irritate the work-driven villagers across the way. I say irritate but I can't remember any kind of contact whatever, friendly or complaining, with the people living nearby. Nor did I ever experience any rowdiness inside the building that might have spilled out to disturb the tranquillity of the local houses. But commonsense suggests otherwise. From the outside there was little to suggest inner harmony and peaceful coexistence.

The Centre consisted of ten or twelve large rooms, most of which radiated haphazardly from a central pillar. They jutted out irregularly to create the uneven angles of the building making it look as though they had been stuck on at different times to serve separate purposes. And this may have been the case because as well as being oddly shaped they were made of various types of material. Red bricks for a couple of them, granite chunks and concrete blocks for others. Some areas of the outside walls carried fading evidence of once having been coated with roughcast and whitewashed. There were lots of windows, all of them covered with rusty iron grills, presumably intended to repel intruders. Otherwise it was difficult to see why they were there at all, the panes of glass behind them having been smashed in long ago and never repaired.

The building's only distinctive architectural feature was a sloping circular secondary roof which stretched down from the top of the central pillar and covered about a quarter of the total area of the main roof. It might have been a grey-slated sunshade floated daintily over the Centre to give a touch of elegance to the squalid cracked walls and broken windows beneath, except for the surprising fact that this upper roof was not simply decorative but functional.

Inside it, there was a small attic with sturdy floorboards and a roof supported by heavy wooden beams, the spokes, in effect, that held the sunshade permanently open. There were no windows in the roof, and no door to the attic, the only means of access being a sturdy wooden ladder which had once been retractable but was now nailed permanently to the ground floor so that the ladder simply disappeared into a hole in the ceiling. This meant that any noise made upstairs could be heard very clearly downstairs. But as none of the rooms at the Centre had doors, it was rare for anyone, up in the attic or down in the main rooms, to complain of loss of privacy or unwelcome intrusion.

Perhaps the Centre had been designed to cater for this kind of openness and for some reason an official decision had once been made to remove all the inside doors. Whether or not, it didn't matter to us how the place came to be as it was or what went on within the dozen or so main rooms. We were too grateful for being allowed free use of the attic several times a week to worry about such trivialities. Why should we care if, as we walked by doorless rooms, we caught glimpses of people inside lifting weights, dancing to music from a portable gramophone, playing table tennis, or sitting on fragile metal-framed chairs solemnly debating topics of the day? We took no notice of them, and they, in turn, tolerated us. It was all in keeping with the topsy-turvy Liberty Hall atmosphere of the place.

Externally the Centre was stark and forbidding. Even the sunshade perched elegantly on high couldn't lessen its grimness. It must have been a constant eyesore to the suburban residents who were forced to live so closely to it. But if they were ever tempted to venture inside they might well have been pleasantly surprised. The rooms were clean, brightly lit, and freshly painted, and although the permanently broken window panes allowed regular gusts of cold air and an occasional spattering of rain to penetrate the building, these wintry effects were countered by an extraordinarily powerful, ancient central-heating system.

Nobody appeared to be in charge. I've no idea how we obtained the right to use the attic, or if we were, in truth, entitled to be there. I like to think that one evening we turned up like the wandering minstrels we in effect were, made good and grateful use of the vacant space, and were allowed to take it over. We were engaged in a form of legalized squatting. Nobody objected to the noise we made. Nobody challenged our right to be there. Nobody tried to occupy what we soon came to regard as our very own room. And nobody ever asked us to sign membership forms or pay a fee.

I now suppose that the Centre must have been set up sometime before the 1939-45 war as an all-purpose community hall, about the same time that many of the houses surrounding it were built. During the war it would probably have been used as temporary accommodation for people living nearby who had been bombed out of their homes. The concrete blocks fixed so incongruously to the some of the original walls might well have been added at the same time as hasty additional protection against air raids.

Then, with the war over, I imagine the Centre reverted to the control of the local council who allowed it, in a manner typical of many such institutions in those world-weary times, to linger on, not because it was positively wanted but because nobody could see any good reason to clear it away. Presumably the council administered the centre, kept it clean, and tacked on the various extensions to meet local recreational needs as and when they arose. Everything was managed from a safe distance and with just enough responsibility to prevent a general collapse. All of this, though, is present-day conjecture. It's what I imagine might have happened. At the time, everything about the place was a mystery to us.

We never knew who washed the linoleumed floors, who cleaned and maintained the primitive green-tiled lavatories, changed the light bulbs, kept the cast-iron radiators at a temperature that made them too hot to lean against even in the coldest weather, or opened the Centre's one outer door in the morning and locked it at night. At least, I assume the Centre closed at night. It was always open for us to use. All I know for certain is that we walked in at certain times of the week, occupied the attic room by custom – there being no posted timetables or rosters – got on with what we went there to do, and left when it was done.

For a period of something like eighteen months I went backwards and forwards to the Centre virtually every Sunday morning and two evenings a week. This was half a century ago in the mid-1950s. When I started going there I would have been fifteen or sixteen years old, still at school, though only just, and that shabby moated grange, hidden mysteriously away in the dense suburbs of south-east London, outwardly scarred but shining bright inside, was the focal point of my life.

* * * *

It's the Sunday visits to the Centre for band sessions that have stayed most luminously with me. On weekdays the experience of getting there was often shared with others. For a while we had a clarinettist, a few years older than the rest of us who worked full time and, remarkably for those years, owned a car. He lived even further away from the Centre than I did, but on weekdays he would come to it straight from work. As that meant passing near to where I lived he would sometimes pick me up. But on Sunday mornings I always found my own way there, choosing to be alone, my emotions concentrated on what was to come. It was possible for me to catch a bus for about half of the journey. That was the easy bit, the part of the journey I still have no trouble remembering. I would only bother with the bus if it happened to come along as I was passing the stop, and that didn't happen often. In those days, early Sunday mornings were vast hollow stretches of silence in which any kind of human noise or activity was angrily discouraged.

Kenny

We lived in an area called Honor Oak Park. It was a popular commuting spot, linked by rail to the centre of London and serviced from early in the morning to late at night by a seemingly endless supply of trains. We had moved to the district shortly after the war. It was to be the family's final occupation of several properties, all of them fitful removals from one part of south London to another, turning us into local refugees, victims of German bombs and doodlebugs. I've never properly understood how the family ended up in a roomy terraced villa in Honor Oak Park. Perhaps the policy of requisitioning private property to deal with the emergency housing shortage during the war was still in operation: perhaps it came about as part of a general postwar rehousing scheme. We were certainly in a state of emergency when we moved into the house, but there was nothing transitional about the move. We stayed there, legally and happily, paying a weekly rent to the local council for many non-emergency years. Whatever the policy, it was regarded with approval by my mother and father, both of whom were implacably opposed to house ownership. That attitude caused no problems locally, even though a fair number of the houses around us were owner occupied. The whole district was remarkably relaxed and socially tolerant, with a strong classless feel about it.

Our semi was three storeys high, with smallish gardens front and back, both left permanently untended, flanked by other very similar houses and set within one of some half-dozen streets lined up in a block of neat rows a couple of hundred yards south of the railway station. On Sunday mornings I would leave the house at about eight o'clock, walk in the opposite direction to the station, through a few more streets much the same as ours, and on to the main road where I could, if I wished, wait for a bus. Discarding that option, I was faced with a walk over a steep hill crowned by a public park, a large unenclosed mix of sparse woods and open green. In a distant corner, there was a children's concrete playground, its swings, roundabouts and rocking horses eerily still and outlined starkly against the early morning sky. I continued down the other side of the hill, out onto the main road again and over a hump-backed bridge that crossed a local railway line. There was then a slight detour round the perimeter of one of London's most popular dog tracks before reaching the point where the bus from home would have dropped me, if I had decided to take it.

And after that, virtually nothing. There must have been another bus journey or, more probably, a walk due south of something like twenty minutes before reaching the Centre. But I can't remember which. My memory, alive to the tiniest detail of the first part of the walk, now gives up on me at about this point and stays blank until I enter an area of long streets lined with small redbrick, red-tiled houses, all with white painted bow windows and glass-panelled front doors. They were similar to the houses that, a little further on, would form a decorative boundary for the Centre. Not all of the inhabitants of these houses were quite as posh as the trim exteriors of their houses were intended to suggest. I knew that because I often visited a schoolfriend who lived in one of the houses, and his family, like mine, was classically urban working class.

Even so, this was part of a suburban world that felt significantly different from that of my own family, a gathering of property owners in tacit agreement that each of them should occupy roughly the same amount of ground, with the same short front gardens and the same long back gardens. They also shared a communal lane at the back of the houses where the few of them capable of taking the next crucial step up the status ladder could garage the family car. Outwardly at least, they were able to cultivate a lower middle-class homogeneity that was alien to Honor Oak Park.

The only drawback to my long dreamy Sunday morning walks was the weight and inconvenient shape of my trumpet case. The weather I hardly ever took into account. I would even traipse blindfold through the thick, filthy autumn and winter fogs that were still common then. Only when the rain was particularly heavy or the slush so messy underfoot that walking was physically difficult would I give up and take the bus. The trumpet case was a more persistent irritant than the weather.

To an outsider this may not sound a serious issue. After all, it's not as though I played the drums or double bass. But then those musicians are expected to take transport into account along with their choice of an instrument. It is, literally, a self-imposed burden they are forced to come to terms with, while a trumpet player is inclined to regard an instrument case as merely functional, utilitarian, a help rather than a hindrance. It was an unusual problem I was faced with, and a personal one as well.

The first instrument I owned had been an ancient cornet obtained in a piece of nifty barter with a sixth-former at school who had become suddenly aware of this strange object lying around the house, unused and apparently unwanted by anyone in his family, a nuisance, just another piece of worthless clutter. The price demanded was a substantial run of *Picturegoer* film magazines in which I no longer had any interest. The cornet was a little battered, but in good enough working order to start on, and it came packed in its own black wooden box of the kind you would see carried by members of a Salvation Army street band on their way to a town centre or street-corner performance. After a while the cornet was displaced in my affections by a second-hand trumpet that was free of dents and glamorously shiny but had no case at all.

I carried it around in a pale blue canvas duffle bag. After a while this gave way to another bag, similar in type to the duffle in that it was fastened by a simple drawstring, but much lighter and floppier. I thought it perfect in every way. It was exactly the right size to hold the trumpet, a mouthpiece and a small plunger mute. In that tired utilitarian age it had the additional attraction, as, of course, jazz itself did, of being out of the ordinary. When the drawstring of the duffle bag was pulled tight it formed a loop large enough to get my hand through. This meant that the trumpet could be safely carried in a variety of ways – casually at my side, hanging down my back, or perched flamboyantly on my shoulder. But what gave it a final classy touch, and made it such a suitable prop for a bit of adolescent display, was the fact that it was made from a piece of very old and faded deep crimson velvet. It was the perfect complement to my new maroon corduroy jacket, contributing just the air of bohemian decoration we were all eager to cultivate.

There was nothing wrong with the bag except in the eyes of my father. He was the problem. Unconsciously and innocently so, but, nevertheless, the problem. He disapproved of the velvet bag, not because it insulted any aesthetic values or even class principles he might have held, but because it was 'scruffy,' not good enough for me, his son.

'I'll make you one,' he promised. 'A case. A proper case. I'll see to it.' And he did, seeing to it in the only manner he understood.

He was a time-served painter and decorator, a highly qualified man in a trade that, along with many others at the time, was on its way to becoming anachronistic. Painting, it was now widely assumed, was a job that pretty well anyone could do. The thought of serving an apprenticeship to it was laughable. Painting didn't even attract much respect among the activities that the new DIY shops were beginning to promote. Being discarded along with once-treasured painterly knowledge and skills were values that had long been regarded as essential elements in an apprentice's training. Chief of these for my father was the conviction that a true workman always took great care of the tools of his trade. This meant cleaning, sharpening, oiling and polishing tools after they had been used in order to keep them in perfect condition. His daytime work, the work that even in good times never brought him more than about ten pounds a week to maintain a wife, four children, and a house, was all too often of the washdown with sugar soap and two coats of emulsion variety, but the tools he used were the same ones he had invested money in before the war as a young man just out of his five-year apprenticeship. Still always lovingly polished, sharpened and preserved they were kept at home in the attic which served him as a workshop for whatever jobs were to be done around the house. For the rest of us it served as a family store and children's playroom.

There was not actually a great deal of painting and decorating done at home. It was understood by all of us that my father who worked all day at a job that was steadily destroying his lungs, could hardly be expected to come home, and cheerfully, as it were, hasten the process. So the house went largely undecorated and unpainted. But there were always other fundamental repairs that couldn't be ignored. As there could be no thought of paying someone to come in and deal with any structural problems that arose my father had to take responsibility for them whether or not he knew what he was doing. Lined up across his workbench or arranged tidily on shelves above it were those tools which had to be on hand for occasions when the highly trained painter and more than competent carpenter was required to apply his terrifyingly primitive skills as an electrician, gas fitter or plumber. There were planes, chisels, hammers, gimlets, screwdrivers, pincers, pliers, mallets, dozens of strangely shaped saws, and set around and underneath the bench, an equally bewildering spread of materials: rolls of wire, flex, tape and chain, lead pipes, brass fittings, cardboard and metal tubes. On one of the shelves, out of the way of immediate use and to my mind too large ever to have been handled by human beings, were two bizarre tools: a carpenter's box plane, and a massive blowtorch, its metal body blackened and twisted.

My father's own tools, the tools of *his* trade, were kept in a wooden chest that was too heavy to serve any purpose other than storage. In it were paint brushes of every size and shape, wallpaper rollers, scissors, knives, wire brushes, bottles of oil, cans of wax, rolls of wire wool and sheets of glass and sand paper. Nothing ever went into the toolchest without first being thoroughly cleaned, dried, and when appropriate, polished or oiled. Around the inside of the chest were fixed strips of canvas, tacked at regular intervals to make loops into which were slotted a variety of knives (for stripping, filling or scraping), together with shave hooks, rules and rulers, and a remarkable collection of oddly shaped specialist paint brushes. Every morning he would take from the chest whichever tools, if any, he was likely to need that day and carry them with him to work in an old shopping bag. He didn't usually bother with a proper toolbox because it would have been far too cumbersome for either the bike or the early morning bus which carried him to work.

When he set about fulfilling his promise to make me a case for my trumpet, he brought to the task all his faith in craftsmanship and the need for every skilled worker to protect the tools of his trade. Unfortunately he followed those principles so steadfastly that he forgot the crucial issue of personal convenience. What I got was a splendid miniature version of the chest in the attic, but while that always remained immovably where it was, the trumpet case had to go everywhere with me.

It was made of top quality quarter-inch white wood and allowed a space inside for about one and a half times the length and depth of a trumpet. The normal commercial trumpet case is rather like a small modern suitcase. It opens round the middle, using either clips or a zip, to reveal the instrument lying on its side, looking, appropriately enough, at rest. My case opened at the top so that you peered down into it to see the trumpet sitting lengthwise and upright, fitted into delicately arched wooden supports that held it tightly in place so that the precious thing wouldn't, *couldn't*, get shaken about. There it stood, poised, ready for action. Stapled round the inside of the case, on the model of the toolchest, was a leather strap shaped into different sized loops for holding mutes, and mouthpieces, and any other accessories. The case was carried by a leather handle set in the middle of the lid which was opened and closed by a heavy brass catch. At the corners of the case, top and bottom, eight in all, were matching brass caps.

I had not been consulted while this extraordinary contraption was being made. When it was finally presented to me I was shockingly aware that it marked the end of a distinct phase of my life. The casualness and studied flamboyance as represented by my faded, elegant, crimson velvet imitation duffle bag were gone for ever. The bag itself I folded and tucked away in a corner of my white-wood coffin. There were, of course, advantages to set against its inconvenient weight and shape, not least the empty space that surrounded the trumpet when it was mounted proudly on its decorative supports. I had had no extra space before. Now I wondered how I ever managed without it. In went all the paraphernalia that could so easily be made to seem essential to the dedicated life of a teenage amateur jazzman. There were mutes and polishing cloths; a large clean handkerchief, not out of fear of a sudden cold developing but in order, if the occasion arose, to hold the trumpet in the approved Louis Armstrong manner; a couple of the latest Penguin paperback poets to pass the time on buses and trains; notebooks containing the titles, keys and basic chords of tunes already played or being learned; and, depending on the weather, a scarf, gloves, even a light sweater.

What finally reconciled me to this handsome awkward object, and the occasionally bruised legs that came with it, was the gradual realization that I had been presented not only with a suitcase and a trumpet case all in one, but a portable bench as well. And much more than simply that, for this was a bench spacious enough for two to perch on, one at each end, on either side of the bulky carrying handle. No self-respecting jazz musician, however young, however limited in musical ability, has ever thought of living a life governed by conventional time or habits, and my case-bench was the perfect companion in the irregular hours I followed from the age of fifteen or so. Very early in the morning, very late at night, at bus stops, in corners of jazz cellars, on railway platforms, huddled against the cold or lounging in the sun, drinking a pint outside a pub, chatting with a fellow jazz musician seated on the other half of the case, having fish and chips for lunch or supper in the open street, reading a book, scribbling a note, it soon became indispensable. In many and various way, it was truly a prop and a comfort; a table, a seat, a desk, a promoter of friendly talk, and, a primitive courting bench as well.

Welcome as all of this was, none of it ever quite erased my awareness that the case was not fulfilling satisfactorily what should have been its prime function. It didn't *look* like a trumpet case, and it certainly didn't help anyone to identify me as a trumpet player. On the contrary, it actually encouraged a kind of banter I could well have done without, and some more purposeful attention.

In those days, policemen, or 'bobbies on the beat' as in future years they were to be nostalgically remembered, were an all too familiar sight on the streets of London, either directing traffic or walking about, singly or in pairs. No doubt they were busily doing what they were traditionally supposed to be doing, telling people the time and providing helpful directions on the quickest way to get here or there. But in my family at least it was well known that what they were really up to was looking for ways to justify their existence.

Our evening dinner table was not infrequently entertained by tales from my father of how he had been stopped by the police on his way home from work and the shopping bag carrying his tools searched for anything they might be able to claim had been pilfered. His narrative style was an equal mix of anger and acceptance, a response of resigned indignation at the abuses suffered by the 'respectable working man' who was simply 'going about his business' trying to 'make a decent living' or 'earn an honest penny.' Phrases such as these which he used all the time owed as much to the music hall (which he adored) as to the Labour Party and his Trade Union (both of which he supported but distrusted). What he wanted was to live his life with a minimum of official interference, so he would have been particularly upset, and I was careful not to let on, that in making me a trumpet case that any time-served man could be proud of he had also passed on to me his hated contacts with the police.

'So, what have you got in there then?'

One on either side. Not threatening. Curious no doubt. Hopeful certainly. It was usually late evening, but it could be early Sunday morning with me on my way to the Centre. They really did pop up everywhere, even among these eerily quiet suburban houses packed with commuters treating themselves to a weekly lie-in. And who could blame a couple of bored bobbies for wondering what on earth I could possibly be up to, strolling by myself through these otherwise empty streets, carrying a white wooden box that bumped clumsily against my legs and appeared to serve no instantly recognizable or worthwhile purpose.

My father's response to the same question, at least in the family version narrated over the dinner table, was always the same: 'What 'ave I got in 'ere? What d'ye think! Me bleedin' tools, that's what.'

It was a fundamental maxim for me, as no doubt it was for most other children of my generation and class, and dinned into me by my father as well as my mother, that if I should ever find myself in trouble of any kind I should go immediately to a policeman, a neat illustration of the fact that they were never far away. But apart from my father's faith in the wonderful ways of policemen with distressed children, he was unshakeably convinced that to a man they were class traitors, employed to walk the streets of London in order to harass, hector, bully, and, whenever the chance arose, frame and lock up honest working men. He himself would proudly use that ancient class cliché at such moments, presenting himself as its epitome. As, in the main, he was.

Always neatly dressed, dapper when the occasion demanded, very hardworking, intellectually curious, gentle and trusted by his employers, he believed that the rest of society was involved in an active conspiracy to keep the ordinary working man poor. He could see no point in trying actively to change the system because it was too firmly rigged against people like him. So he asserted the inviolability of working-class life. Anyone approaching it from the outside was regarded with suspicion and hostility. Politicians and trade unionists were only in it for what they could get; charity and social workers were do-gooders; the church was always 'on the ear 'ole ' (i.e. scrounging for money).

This kind of cynicism was a result of my father's constant struggle to earn enough money to keep his family alive. So stifling was his inability to embrace any kind of life beyond the immediate moment, apart possibly from the dreamy financial transformation that might come about from winning the pools, that it even prevented him from wholeheartedly supporting the single coherent family policy that dominated all of our lives. In true Lawrentian mode, it was my mother who believed, and who followed the belief with missionary fervour, that education was the way to escape the borderline poverty within which she feared we would otherwise be trapped for ever. That solution was, of course, for the children, not for her or my father. Neither of them had had any formal education beyond the age of twelve or so, and there was no point in even thinking of their situation ever changing. Education was for the children. It was the only way out. When in a cynical mood, my father regarded teachers as part of the social conspiracy, all set to prevent his children for as long as possible from going out to work and contributing, for a few short years at least, to the family kitty. As my mother would have nothing at all to do with such a view, his role in her grand strategy was to enable us all to survive long enough to reach the promised land. The obstacles were formidable.

Being stopped on his way home from a hard day's work to have his shopping/tool bag searched by people who had 'never done a good day's work in their lives,' my father regarded as typical police behaviour. It was humiliating and insulting, and there was nothing to be done about it. To object, quarrel or respond angrily was the surest way of being carried off to the station. That is why his anecdotes about the police would concentrate on the lying, hypocritical, interfering pointlessness of the standard question 'What have you got in there then?' This was becoming another weary cliché, made so not by class values but by radio and film comedy and soon to be camped out of court by a new generation of brilliant comic actors like Peter Sellers and Kenneth Williams. My father, though, was not drawn to its funny side. As he would explain, the coppers knew bloody well what he was carrying in his bag. They only asked because they wanted to be proved wrong.

Although my own exchanges with the police were fundamentally the same as his, their tone with me was very different. Things were changing, and I don't mean in the police force.

There I was carrying my trumpet case along one of the tidy owner-occupied suburbs of south London. Very young, grammar-school accent, unfashionably long hair, dressed in the regulation classless clothes of teenagers with my musical and literary interests at that time – duffle coat, chunky sweater, corduroy trousers, suede shoes – which had been bought largely with money earned from a Saturday morning job, I was very obviously *not* a working man. Honest I might or might not still be. In normal circumstances that particular doubt would have been applied automatically to my father, but not to me. It only arose now because of the suspiciously bulky object I was carrying. If I could afford to be amused rather than angry at police interference it was because I knew there was no chance of me getting into trouble with them.

While they were pretty sure what my father had in his shopping bag and were challenging him only to cause trouble, they had no way of knowing what was in my wooden box. They weren't offering a question to which they already had the answer, but one which expressed their genuine puzzlement.

'So, what have you got in there then?'

'A trumpet.'

'A trumpet.'

'Uh, uh.'

'Who are you then, Eddie Calvert? How about a quick burst of "Cherry Pink and Apple Blossom White"?'

'I'd rather die than play like Eddie Calvert.'

'You could do worse.'

'Not much.'

'All right! Open it up. Let's have a look.'

And that was it. Once they'd seen the trumpet balanced perkily on its wooden supports, any doubts they might genuinely have had, faded away. It was the obvious discrepancy between musical instrument and container that saved the situation. This couldn't possibly be stolen property. The combination was too odd to be anything other than genuine. Sometimes they were even interested enough to have a chat. What was wrong with Eddie Calvert? Why didn't I like him when everyone else in the country was mad about him. Who could be better than him? They also wanted to know where I was off to at that time on a Sunday morning. They always knew of the Centre. It may have been, I now imagine, somewhere they had orders to keep an official eye on. If so, their surveillance wasn't very effective because the Centre was as much a mystery to them as it was to me. What exactly did we do there? Were there girls? Dancing? Could people come and listen? I was happiest when they asked what kind of music we played. On that topic I was willing to inform them, or anyone else, endlessly.

One of the strange things about these exchanges with the police is that if they had questioned my father about what I was carrying in my large wooden box at such an odd hour in this sleepy respectable neighbourhood he would probably have answered in a quite untroubled manner. He might even have been eager to provide them with some information. Of course they had no right to interfere. All they were doing was being their normal intrusive selves. But on this occasion they were obviously not trying to prevent a decent working man from going about his legitimate business, and, as they were in the wrong, there would have been an opportunity for my father to show off a little. Even so, they would have found his response even more peculiar than mine.

It would have been something like: 'That's Peter, my second son. He's going to a jam session. He always does on Sunday mornings. That's his trumpet he's got in there. I made the case especially for him. He's a jazz trumpeter, just like Bunk Johnson.'

My father, you see, was incapable of making the policeman's dreadful gaffe about Eddie Calvert, but still, and I need to move cautiously here for some crucial distinctions are involved, my father's proudly announced point of reference would not have been exactly correct. His error, though, was acceptable enough. It was at one with the trumpet case itself in that it derived from a lethal parental brew of pride, love, and wholly uncritical sympathy.

As far as my father was concerned Bunk Johnson *was* jazz. He knew well enough that other jazz musicians existed, though I don't think he was ever really able to distinguish one from another. Bunk came first, and all the rest, whatever their musical distinction or affiliation, followed behind. Ranking of jazz musicians would for him have been solely a matter of how much influence they had exerted on the family, and considered from this angle there was no one to match Bunk Johnson. He had started it all. He was the one who had stirred up the transforming enthusiasm in Harry, the eldest son of the house, which had then spread through and captivated the whole family. It mattered little that other favourites quickly emerged. Bunk was the instigator, and there was no way he could ever be replaced. Stick firm with Bunk, I can imagine my father reasoning. He will see us through.

The jazz trumpeter I was 'just like' was American, black, and had been dead for some years. He came from New Orleans, and had been born around 1880. When exactly nobody seemed to know. His widely reported death, though, had been in 1949, recently enough for the whole of my family to be aware of the event. Many years later, clearing away some family papers I came across an obituary cut neatly from the *Melody Maker*. I would have been ten years old at the time it was written and still a year or two off from beginning to develop an interest in jazz, so it must have been Harry who had chosen to keep a documentary record of this historic moment, and my father, presumably, who had preserved it.

For us, Bunk Johnson wasn't just a figure in American music. He was a legend, though, of course, we were all too aware of him as also belonging to a very specific historical place and time. This was New Orleans, Louisiana where jazz was born some time in the last two decades of the nineteenth century. But we also accepted unquestionably that he belonged to all of us in Honor Oak Park. He travelled through space and time, adapting or adjusting his image to local conditions much as the gods of the ancient world had done. My father would have made his announcement of my similarity to Bunk Johnson with total pride and no sense whatever of temporal, cultural, national, or racial differences.

In the early 1950s, black faces were very rarely seen in Honor Oak Park. None of us, I'm sure, knew anyone who was black, though Harry might occasionally have come across a West Indian immigrant in the jazz clubs he went to, and my father would probably have met black American soldiers in the war, though if so I don't remember him mentioning them. It was even part of family lore that a not too distant family relative had 'married a black man' and by all accounts was living very happily with him somewhere in North London. What kind of black man he was we never learned, and we never would, because my mother wasn't happy about *her* children mixing with anyone at all outside our immediate family circle, relatives or not and whatever colour they might have been.

Not that Bunk was ever thought of in connection with this distant black relative of ours. Bunk, like Ulysses or Neptune, was busily getting on with the task of fulfilling his mythological function, moving casually among people of totally different cultures, effortlessly changing the meaning and emotion of their lives. He wasn't even regarded as part of the general Americanization of popular entertainment that was already on the way to taking over the whole country. We'd all pretty well succumbed to American films and we knew how potent they could be, especially when allied with popular music. This came to us through a more open side of our otherwise home-fixated mother.

She was obsessed with the music of Al Jolson, or, more precisely, the music of Al Jolson as mimed to by the film actor Larry Parks. As children we were taken to see the two celebrated biopics *The Jolson Story* and *Jolson Sings Again* at every possible opportunity. My mother liked to claim she had seen these films dozens of times, and I'm sure she wasn't exaggerating. Nowadays it is all too easy to clock up an impressive number of repeat viewings simply by sitting at home with a VCR or DVD. But for my mother every single viewing meant a special trip to the pictures, most of them involving a determined effort and a careful calculation whether the expense was justifiable. She would have first seen the films when they were featured at our smarter cinemas in the neighbouring districts of Forest Hill or Lewisham and again and again and again when rerun at the local flea pit. She also made one legendary trip to the West End to see a special double performance of the two films. As she was far too prim ever to think of going to the pictures by herself, my father must have accompanied her on some of these outings, and when he was unable or unwilling to do so, she dragged one or other of us children along with her.

I was her enforced companion often enough on these outings to still remember the names of the main actors and actresses and the parts they played. And that's not all. I can whistle the tunes, and, if challenged, make a fair go of stumbling through the lyrics of many of the famous Al Jolson songs such as 'Back in Your Own Backyard,' 'Sonny Boy,' 'I Only Have Eyes for You,' 'My Mammy,' and 'Toot, Toot, Tootsie.' There were 78rpm records of Al Jolson in the house, though where they came from I've no idea. Presents, I suppose, from my father or Harry. Certainly my mother wouldn't have bought them. She would have died from the shame of spending the few shillings they would have cost on herself rather than on her children.

Wherever they came from, the 78s were around and we played them constantly. They were part of a small miscellaneous family collection which featured Bunk Johnson of course, and also Harry James, Bing Crosby, Sid Phillips, and Danny Kaye. They were played on a wind-up gramophone long before we could afford a modern record player. The very first ten-inch LP that came into the house, or that any of us had ever seen, featured Al Jolson. It was a present to my mother from one of my cousins who had managed to infiltrate the inner family circle by becoming close friends with Harry. He had heard about LPs and felt straightaway that my mother simply had to be told about this new way of gaining extended access to her musical hero. The old two-and-a-half or three-minute-and-twenty-seconds days were over. We didn't have a machine on which we could play the miraculous thing, but we did have the LP itself. It was kept as a treasured object for a long time before we could make any use of it.

The music of Al Jolson does have some historical connections with jazz, though today they tend, understandably, to be forgotten or marginalized. We knew of them and were careful not to take them seriously or to confuse the true with the false. In other words, we were quite clear that there was little in common between Al Jolson and Bunk Johnson. When it came to the language of jazz we were all pedants in our family. We would never have allowed anyone in our hearing to get away with referring to Al Jolson as 'The Jazz Singer' or have permitted anyone to call Paul Whiteman 'The King of Jazz' without intervening with the essential correction. These were shocking solecisms perpetrated by the unenlightened that needed to be crushed whenever they appeared. Our inflexibility on such matters caused the whole family much trouble with outsiders.

The Jolson interest we accepted as part of the early growth of fandom, all calculated adoration, blind acceptance, celebrity worship, weeping and wailing after false gods. In contrast, jazz was an art form. Never, right from the beginning, did any of us doubt that. All we had to compare it with was the popular music we heard on radio variety shows; the music-hall songs sung to us with great enthusiasm by our paternal grandmother; and, increasingly, American cinema and pop music. Classical music we knew only through the popular extracts which were featured regularly on radio variety or record-request programmes. All of this music was accepted casually as part of the everyday atmosphere, to be dismissed or enjoyed as the case may have been. But the only appropriate response to jazz was serious appreciation. It was a matter of discrimination and choice, demanding the same kind of approach as the books and paintings that were also being experienced and discussed not so much at home, but avidly within my small circle of close school friends. Had any of us been aware of the possible comparison, we would have been aware even then that jazz was our (and first and foremost, of course, America's) very own classical music.

My mother's approach to Al Jolson was an entirely different thing. It was not only uncritical, it was beyond criticism, untouchable. In her thirties and responsible for four adored children she may have been, but in the cinema she sat watching Larry Parks in what can only be described as the swooning mood of a footloose teenager. If Parks, or Jolson himself, had ever appeared at a London theatre I expect she would have joined hundreds of other women at the stage door, tugging away at her hair and sobbing deliriously. She would then have come straight home to her crowded kitchen and freezing-cold, stone-floored scullery and got on with the cooking or washing or ironing.

It was that element of conscious fantasy that most clearly separated the two musicians who dominated our home in the early and mid-1950s. Or so we supposed. The distinction was there all right, if not quite as obvious as we assumed. There was no doubt, though, about the fantasy element. Jolson was distant glamour brought up close, manipulative Hollywood escapism, directed consciously at older women, my mother being, I suppose, a typical fan. What he did for her, in a phrase she herself would often use in other contexts, was to 'take her out of herself,' and for doing that I will never believe that Jolson deserved anything but enormous credit. In a life as hard as hers, and short, as, all but inevitably, it turned out to be, here was something she greatly enjoyed and needed. The fact that it had clear emotional boundaries and was supported, or at least tolerated sympathetically, by her husband and children made its existence possible.

I was too young to have wondered whether my mother's Jolson-inspired fantasies could have contained a sexual element. I now assume they must have done. While working away endlessly in the house, she might well have dreamt of being romantically or sexually linked with Larry Parks, who was famously handsome, though Al Jolson himself still seems to me to be an unlikely candidate. I would never have thought of my mother as having an inner life of her own, but of course she did, and although totally closed to me, it wouldn't have been such a mystery to my father. If she was in danger of drifting a little too far away from reality, he was there to tease her with a reminder that Al Jolson was a blacked-up, white, Jewish, Russian, American who had never looked anything like Larry Parks. Was there at such moments a touch of resentment at his wife being so romantically attached to this manufactured celluloid hybrid? If so, it would have been too slight, and he was too loving a husband, to challenge the dream. I'd be happy to settle for it being the shared singing voice alone which worked the magic, if only she hadn't been so eager to seize on biographical details from the films and mull them over, much as tabloid newspapers do today about events in television soap operas.

She treated characters in the films as though they were members of our own wider family whose behaviour demanded close attention on her part. Was Jolson's first wife, played by Evelyn Keyes, right to walk out on him? Shouldn't she have understood that show business was Jolson's life, and that she could only have him at all by playing a secondary role? He may have been wrong to ignore her feelings when called upon by adoring fans to sing while she was left sitting alone at their night-club table, but what else could she expect, and what on earth would she do without him anyway? How extraordinary it was that she should just walk out of the film/his life in that stubborn manner, and how lucky Jolson was to be able to rely on the support of his wonderful friend and agent played by William Demarest.

Bunk Johnson was clearly not a product of Hollywood. The kind of glamour he possessed had nothing to do with the conventional show business or Parksian sense of having marketable sex appeal. It derived entirely from his legendary status. And why not? He was a glamorous legend because jazz itself was legendary and glamorous, not just a music but a mythology, a way of life, a collection of startling tales that claimed to express the nature of this strange unparalleled music that had arrived so devastatingly among us. Everything we knew about Bunk made his mythological status irresistibly compelling. His story contained exactly what we wanted to believe about jazz. He, and it, was expansive, revealing possibilities that were totally removed from anything we had known previously and yet fully convincing us that here was something in which we could both believe and participate.

In contrast, Al Jolson was self-contained, individual enough in himself, but a sort of pod. The life and the music being sold to his fans were ersatz experience, easily duplicated by many other similar commercially promoted figures. Friends of my own age who had no interest in jazz tended to regard both Jolson and my Jolson-worshipping mother as a joke, but then they themselves had bought into their own commercially promoted and far less talented idols. These were men or women, stars of film and records, usually in their thirties, American or Americanized-British, with not a tinge of jazz anywhere in their music. They were not blacked-up certainly, but hardly ever authentically black either. We thought the whole lot of them as not worth joking about.

And although Bunk Johnson was also American, he represented a way of life that was as alien to Hollywood and Tin Pan Alley as it was to south London. It should, therefore, have felt strange to us, but it never did. Bunk not only entered our lives and formed our musical taste, he also promised, as it were, to stay with us, to allow us to become like him, and what could be better than that? This is why my father seemed barely aware that Bunk was either black or American. 'This is my second son Peter. He's a jazz trumpeter just like Bunk Johnson.' It didn't indicate any lack of awareness on my father's part. Bunk may have had his own carefully promoted image to project, and more so than any of us would have suspected at the time, but it was still inseparable from both his music and the life that music epitomized. What he offered was closer to revealed religion than Hollywood fandom. He wasn't distant, polished, or set apart. He assured us that what he did we could also do, and we instantly set out to follow his example. The fact that everything about the music was foreign to our personal experiences was irrelevant. We weren't conscious of making a choice, of saying, let's try this rather than that. What other remotely comparable choices were there? We were taken over by it. It became instantly *our* music.

My generation was not the first in Britain to absorb these feelings and values. We were not pioneers. There had been individual musicians inspired by American jazz ever since the early 1920s when it had first travelled to Europe, but it was only from the late 1930s onwards as the revivalist movement took off in America that a significant number of British musicians set out consciously to play or to revive or recreate, as they themselves would have described their activity, what came to be called 'traditional' jazz. Some of the most prominent names were George Webb, Ian and Keith Christie, Humphrey Lyttleton, Wally Fawkes, Cy Laurie, Chris Barber, Ken Colyer. These were all based in the south of England but the movement was by no means limited geographically. In Scotland there were the notable figures of Sandy Brown, Al Fairweather, and Alex Welsh, all of whom moved south to pursue London-based careers. Other musicians stayed where they were to establish bands which built up strong local reputations: the Saints in Manchester, and others whose names proudly advertised their home bases: the Clyde Valley Stompers, the Yorkshire Jazzband, the Merseysippi Jazzmen. Similar developments were taking place across Europe, but not apparently, we whispered to each other, in America.

That was decidedly odd, though it did appear to be true that America was little interested in the only kind of jazz we thought mattered. The one exception we were familiar with tended to support rather than disprove our doubts. This was Lu Watters and his Yerba Buena Jazz Band based in California. It was a classic revivalist band, modelled, as its British and European equivalents also were, on King Oliver and Louis Armstrong, and had made recordings with Bunk himself. Yet even a pedigree as authentic as this could not change our conviction that somewhere along the way American bands like the Yerba Buena had got it wrong. What they played was good-time music, a form of white Dixieland that was a bit too raucous for us. It was brash, tipping over at times into the corny. There was not enough seriousness involved, insufficient awareness that they were involved in a mission to preserve greatness, even to keep true jazz alive, missionary qualities that their British equivalents possessed in abundance.

One reason why our prejudices and mistaken assumptions flourished so easily was because there were very few published books available at the time to supply us with reliable information. What little we knew came in the main from cheaply produced discographies and slim pamphlets with educational titles like *One Hundred Essential Facts about Jazz*. Nor were there all that many records to listen to. It was quite common for us to read about, or refer to, musicians and performances that we had no chance of hearing for ourselves. Our knowledge of jazz we picked up as we went along; scraps of information, whether factual or mythological, and inspired above all by a slow, sporadic drip-feed of 78s. So eager were we to nourish our narrowness on whatever meagre food was available that we allowed ourselves to be all but totally, sometimes proudly, ignorant of newer developments in jazz, or indeed of any other kinds of jazz at all. Our assumptions were reinforced by the traditional jazz scene that was already going on actively around us.

All of the pioneering British trad musicians were white, while the music they played was overwhelmingly black. In the main, they were between ten and twenty years older than us. By the mid-1950s when we were starting up, they were firmly establishing themselves as the leaders in this type of music, a position they were always to maintain. A decade later, some of them would be responsible for taking the music on a small number of spectacular forays into the hit parade. They developed several slightly different types of traditional jazz, and came to epitomize them. In terms of musical affiliation there was hardly a gap between them and us. They had been attracted by the same mythology, their models and inspirations were the same as ours, and in our fumbling, intuitive, blindly devoted amateur way, we simply followed on, blending together the American originals and the British revivalists.

Even so, we were still set apart from the British pioneers, socially if not musically. That ten or fifteen years age difference placed them closer to our parents' generation than ours, something it was impossible for us not to be aware of. We were postwar in ways they weren't, teenagers in ways they never had been, and therefore part of the youth culture that emerged so forcefully in the 1950s to which they never belonged. Given this, it's the more extraordinary that there was a complete absence of any generational clash between us. In fact, quite the opposite was true. On our part there was only admiration. We didn't want to be different from them, but the same. Musically, our ambition was to do exactly what they were doing, which was imitating earlier American black jazz. And although some of the best of our generation moved up to join the ranks of the pioneers, that was as near as we ever got to matching their achievements. What we did collectively, though, was in a special way even more remarkable. Not least, because it was largely unconscious.

With their example constantly to hand, we were the first postwar British teenagers to embrace and emulate black American music to the virtual exclusion of all else. That example has continued unbroken, and no doubt more forcefully and certainly more self-consciously than anything we could ever have imagined, to the present day. Because it moved so swiftly into or was displaced by more popular and more commercially lucrative forms of music, the role played by traditional jazz in the wider process has tended to be sidelined. It was barged out of the way by, among others, Bill Haley, Elvis Presley, and the Beatles, all of whom were also white imitators of essentially black music.

But, like it or not, traditional jazz was where it all started in Britain. There have been quite a few odd twists and turns in the story since then, and it's by no means my intention to try to trace any of them here. It's the beginnings that interest me; the curiosity of our musical passions, our devotion and dedication; the ambiguities and contradictions that were inevitably cast up for us to confront. Not many of today's established musicians in contemporary British popular music, black or white, will know much about traditional jazz. Nor will they regard Bunk Johnson as one of their great predecessors. Very few of them are likely even to have heard of him. But for us there were good reasons why both his life and his music were inspirational. This was the story, true or not, that we treasured.

* * * *

In the late 1930s, with Swing the current hot music craze and what would come to be called modern jazz on its way, a number of American and European jazz enthusiasts set themselves the task of trying to track down certain jazz musicians who were once renowned in and around New Orleans but had since disappeared from view. Bunk Johnson was high on the wanted list. He was believed to have been a contemporary of revered New Orleans trumpeters like Buddy Bolden, the unchallenged first King of New Orleans, and Freddie Keppard who should, by rights, have taken over Bolden's crown when he became incapable of holding on to it, but who, for some unknown reason, failed in the succession. As a teenager in the final years of the nineteenth century, Bunk had actually played with Bolden, and a few years on he himself had been followed admiringly through the streets by a very young Louis Armstrong. In return for carrying the Master's cornet when he needed a rest, Louis had received lessons from him. That, at least and among lots of similar things, was what was said, and what we all faithfully repeated to each other and to anyone else who would listen.

Armstrong was now a world-famous celebrity, developing an image as Ambassador Satch, the touring representative of jazz at its most popular, a bit too popular for some of us at the time. Back in New Orleans, after Bunk had helped him on his way to a spectacular early reputation, Armstrong had been invited to Chicago to join King Oliver's Creole Jazz Band. Oliver's greatness was soon wiped out by ill health, but it was there for anyone to acknowledge on dozens of gramophone records, many of the best of them featuring the young Louis as well. Freddie Keppard had been more cautious, or perhaps less ambitious, than Oliver and Armstrong. He wanted to be admired but feared it would undermine his freedom to play as he pleased. One strategy he adopted to prevent this happening was to drape a handkerchief over the valves of his trumpet so that wannabe Keppards couldn't observe his fingering. He also had serious reservations about the newfangled gramophone. Apparently, he could have been the first jazz musician to record, but he turned down the invitation. He thought the whole business of gramophones was stupid. Put your music on those things, he claimed, and everyone will copy it. And goodness, how right, in the fullness of time and in ways he could never have foreseen, he would turn out to be!

Nevertheless, once he saw the success that recording had brought to his rivals, he followed them to the studios, making a handful of records before his death in 1930 which give us some idea of how he sounded. It remains a fancy of mine that 'Stock Yards Strut' by Keppard's Jazz Cardinals, recorded in 1926, is probably as near as we will ever get to knowing what New Orleans small-group jazz was really like back at the start of it all in the closing years of the nineteenth century. Buddy Bolden was never given the chance to visit a recording studio. Famed for the hotness of his trumpet playing and the wildness of his personal life, he went insane during a New Orleans street march, an early spectacular departure from the jazz scene that ensured he would remain forever unchallenged as the most impenetrable of the New Orleans legends.

Essentially, all that was ever going to be known about these great figures was, we assumed, already available. Their names were engraved on the rolls. It was their long neglected near contemporary survivors who were now being hunted down, musicians who had not succumbed to the alcoholism, sexual disease and physical violence endemic in New Orleans, and who had not been seduced by the shining lights and gold of Chicago.

There must still be, it began to be argued, a fair number of them around. Unlike some other golden ages, it was known for sure that this one had existed, and not all that long ago. A musician from the early days who had managed to stay alive would still only be in his fifties or sixties. Revered figures like Armstrong and Sidney Bechet and Kid Ory fitted the pattern. So did Jelly Roll Morton who claimed to have invented jazz. Nobody believed that, but still he had made celebrated recordings throughout his life, and, no doubt, would have gone on doing so if he had not, it was rumoured, been wasted away by a voodoo curse in 1941. And there was Tommy Ladnier, often hailed as one of the revivalists' great discoveries, though he had actually made records as a young man and died in 1939 just as the new interest in early jazz was beginning to take off.

None of these figures quite fitted the revivalists' agenda. What they were looking for were musicians who would be able to clarify whether jazz always had been the kind of music as played by Oliver, Armstrong, and Morton. In other words, were those great figures – and no one was denying their greatness – true pioneers? Wasn't it just possible that the musicians from New Orleans who had been so eagerly courted and fêted by Chicago and New York, and whose commercial success had spawned all the phoney 'Jazz Singers' and 'Kings of Jazz,' as well as the current crowd-pleasing swing idols like Benny Goodman and Harry James, had left behind them a related, though significantly different, type of jazz? Put crudely – and crudity, though deeply felt, was pretty much the order of the day – had they or had they not sold out?

Bunk Johnson was perfectly fitted to test the theory. According to his own account, he would have been anything up to twenty years old when Louis Armstrong was born. He had been much talked of and admired as a trumpeter in those early days, and had stayed in the Crescent City, avoiding possible musical corruption by northern commercialism. Most impressive of all, he had never been recorded. There was only verbal evidence to assess what his trumpet playing had once sounded like. All the signs were favourable. In the word that was soon to take on huge resonance in British jazz circles, he was 'pure.'

When the revivalists succeeded in tracking him down they found that he was poor as well as pure, in bad health, trumpetless, toothless, argumentative, and rather too fond of a drink. None of this did anything to deflate the ardour of his supporters. With the money raised, they helped restore his health, bought him a set of false teeth (our favourite detail this, repeated endlessly among us) and presented him with a trumpet which some said had been paid for by Louis Armstrong. Around him they gathered a group of musicians who had also in the main stayed in New Orleans. They were unpolished (nothing wrong with that), full of jazz spirit (everything right with that), and included among their number George Lewis, a clarinettist, also previously unrecorded, who could match Bunk's quality and purity and would eventually succeed him as the leading inspirational guide for jazz purists throughout the world.

The truly astonishing thing was that when the primitive recording apparatus was switched on, first in New Orleans in 1942 and then in New York three years later, Bunk Johnson and his New Orleans Band came up with precisely what was expected of them. The most ardent of revivalists couldn't have asked for more. They were delirious with self-righteousness. Nobody had gall enough to claim that what they were now hearing was not intimately related to the music already long familiar from gramophone records, but then it was just as obviously not quite the same thing either. The faithful had argued, on little hard evidence, that jazz had once been like this, and now, miraculously, here it was just as they had said it should be. It was, at one and the same time, old and new. Although often foretold, nothing exactly like it had been heard before. It was an archaeological as well as a musical triumph.

What most impressed was the band's sense of togetherness, with probably more attention being given to ensemble playing than on any recordings since those by King Oliver's Creole Jazz Band in the early 1920s. Even that comparison prompted as many differences as similarities. The leading members of the Creole Jazz Band seemed always to be straining to break free from any restraint placed upon them, as though they could barely wait to seize for themselves the opportunity for virtuoso expression. And that, of course, is what they, and the other Chicago and New York based musicians had soon done. The bands led by Armstrong, Morton, Fletcher Henderson, Luis Russell and the rest, became showcases for brilliant displays, individual as well as collective. For them, ensemble playing was soon little more than the setting for wonderfully imaginative solos and breaks. The limitations of early records dictated that a dance-hall performance of a musical number that may have lasted for anything between ten minutes and half an hour had to be limited to two and a half or three minutes in a recording studio. Musicians accustomed to long stretches of spontaneous improvisation were now allowed at most a single chorus, sometimes only a two or four bar break. This meant anything between ten and forty-five seconds to make their musical statement. The constraints were daunting, but, as so often in all art forms, finding ways round the restrictions proved a source of inspiration. In feats of breath-taking virtuosity allied with remarkable self-control, the best of these early records were the musical equivalents of great lyric poems or framed paintings, each part contributing something distinctive to the overall pattern. They were perfectly unified moments of expression, packed with brief unforgettable snatches of individual creativity, fixed in that form for ever, impossible to think of as being played in any other way.

Bunk and his sidemen were no more about musical power or individual flamboyance than they were about commercial success. The solos and breaks they took were there to provide variety rather than to demonstrate individual brilliance. Ensemble was the essence of their music. It was only when they blended together that they produced their own brand of lyricism. Bunk's contribution was essential. His playing was sweet rather than hot. There were attempts to explain this away in terms of his years of not playing at all, his frail health, or those wonderful false teeth, as though it was undesirable for a trumpeter to offer a band anything but a fiery lead. In fact his sweetness was a positive. In the early days, Bunk had been famous for his tone. Now, years later, here it was, a bit ragged at first, and sometimes quite a bit too staccato, but at best smoothing itself out and contributing a defining roundness to the band's overall sound.

With so much communal emphasis, the clarinet seized for itself a new kind of prominence, gliding and swooping across the ensemble, moving from high to low register, providing a lyrical voice that more than compensated for the thumping rhythm of piano, drums, banjo, and bass. It reasserted the original distribution of instrumental roles in the New Orleans marching bands, the classic tripartite balance of bass (trombone), tenor (trumpet) and soprano (clarinet) on which the earliest jazz bands had been based. It was all so wonderfully true, so obviously the real thing, a rediscovery, a survival, a revival.

Not everyone agreed. Some critics enjoyed claiming that the emphasis on togetherness was less a return to the basic values of New Orleans jazz than an illustration of the desperate need for Bunk and his sidekicks to cling together in order to stop themselves from falling over. OK, perhaps it was genuine, but so what? Why put such faith in these particular musicians? After all, they were getting on a bit, some of them hadn't played regularly for years, and they were stuck in the past. It wasn't hard to see why most of them had stayed in New Orleans. They weren't good enough to be invited anywhere else. They were trapped in a social and musical time warp. Why believe they would have been capable of development if they had been given the chance? To be honest, they weren't much good, were they? The splits and divisions, heresies and schisms arose immediately, and if this is beginning to sound like the language of old-time religion, well, so it should. The true and the false; the pure and the impure; and no compromise. That's what it was all about.

We quickly divided ourselves into two musical extremes. On the one hand there were Trads (traditionalists) and on the other Mods (modernists). That is, those who were happy to stay forever within the kind of jazz created in New Orleans and Chicago up until, say, about 1930, and those who placed their allegiance firmly with the Bebop revolution of the 1940s associated with musicians such as Dizzy Gillespie, Charlie Parker and Bud Powell. Trad and Mod were boundary markers. In between there were various types of jazz, ranging from Dixieland to Swing. There was also a good deal of miscellaneous small-group jazz which often featured musicians from the big bands. It was highly polished and accomplished, eclectic, picking and mixing from all kinds of jazz and was beginning to be called Mainstream. At first it was associated with America, but it soon spread to Europe, attracting musicians who were drawn to its broad-mindedness and easy swinging ways. Here was something to escape *into*, a way out of narrowness and ideological fervour. For those who were satisfied with fervour, mainstream was seen as exactly that, a retreat for glib, over-polished defectors who lacked faith, a pagan hotchpotch of styles.

My own allegiance was clear. I was a Trad. At school, aged about fifteen, I had a friend who was a Mod. My battered cornet was then a newly acquired, proud possession and I was just beginning to be able to squeeze a couple of simple tunes out of it that were almost recognizable, 'Careless Love' probably, and 'When the Saints go Marching In.' My modernist friend's equivalent object of pride and devotion was an alto sax. He played phrases or riffs rather than tunes, perhaps because that was all he could manage, or perhaps, as I assumed, because there weren't any tunes in modern jazz. Neither of us, as yet, had developed any kind of control over our respective instruments, but occasionally, during school dinner times, we would escape together to his nearby house and in his back garden blast a few primitive notes at each other. This was all the communication we could manage. 'Bunk meets Bird,' a session to dream of, or to have nightmares about! They were great dinner times, and notable for a curious absence of hostility between the two of us. Curious, because once out of my friend's back garden, and returned up the hill to school, whenever and wherever we happened to meet, in the playground or corridors, in streets or classrooms, contact between us was largely restricted to him snarling 'Trad!' at me, while I would respond with derisory howls of 'Mod!' at him.

I'm sure that this seemingly odd friendship was fairly typical, being confrontational, partisan, and committed, while at the same time self-conscious enough to be treated by both sides as at least worthy of a touch of irony. Beyond the inner circle, there was an assumption that being a Trad was little more than a forgivable adolescent phase, something to be quickly grown out of. Musically speaking, any personal or technical change was regarded as entirely one-way, involving as it inevitably did, a development from the crude to the sophisticated, from traditional to modern, or, a little later and more commonly, from traditionalism to the broad church of mainstream. Some might drop *down* from modernism into mainstream, but never, in my experience, all the way down to traditionalism. This was rendered impossible by the feelings of musical superiority on the part of the Mods, while they in return were regarded by the Trads as being perversely addicted to mere musical technique, all flashy skill and no emotion. Changeovers, conversions, and defections did take place, and they could be very serious matters, long felt and not easily forgiven.

At some point in the mid-1950s I became caught up in a bit of commerce with a fellow schoolboy who had gone over to the enemy. He had made it known that he wanted to stock up on the new sounds and dump the old, so I gathered whatever loose cash I could get my hands on and went round to his house which turned out to be not much larger than ours but smarter in ways that were unfamiliar to me. The floors were heavily carpeted, and there were pieces of highly polished furniture dotted around that seemed to have no obvious everyday function. His parents had handed the dining room over to him as a temporary office. There we waited for a few minutes while his mother draped a candlewick cloth over a brilliantly shiny circular table. Her son then transferred several small batches of his redundant 78s, already neatly arranged according to bands and types of jazz, from the sideboard to the table.

We tried to pretend that our business transactions were to be taken seriously, but it didn't work. How could it? We were asking each other to set a fixed value on objects which, depending on current passions, were either priceless or worthless. The market in operation here was no different from any other. Price depended on the degree or intensity of desire provoked, and we soon abandoned any thought of sophisticated negotiation and reverted happily to the only kind of trade we both understood. This was the raw passion of schoolboy barter, the desperate longing to obtain what someone else currently possesses, children swapping a run of comics for a water pistol, a champion conker for two bars of chocolate, or indeed cinema fanzines for an ancient cornet.

In this instance, my carefully saved one-shilling, two-shilling, and half-crown pieces, were matched against the neat stacks of records. They were there, as we both knew, because the sound they produced which had once thrilled him now seemed unacceptably outmoded. The money, as such, was of no interest to either of us. It would have suited him if I really had been in a position to barter because anything he could manage to squeeze out of me was going to be spent immediately on new records by a trumpet player I had never heard of called Fats Navarro. Selling his collection had, therefore, a very specific and practical purpose. It was, though, symbolic as well, a visible demonstration of his current belief that from this moment on all jazz trumpeters earlier than Navarro were to be pronounced over and done with. Everybody else was old hat, finished.

He insisted on playing his most recent Navarro acquisition in an attempt to convert me. It was a generous move. After all, if he had succeeded I would have had no further interest in buying the records I was already eagerly examining and he would have had no money to buy more Fats Navarro. His generosity of spirit did not, though, awaken a similar response in me. All I could hear was a harsh unmusical tone and a frantic demonstration of pointless technique. Those same qualities, given a positive interpretation quite beyond me, made him so eager to buy more records by his new hero that he volunteered to dispense with all the rest of his dead oldies as a job lot. My finances wouldn't run to the sum of money he named, but we did persevere for a little longer, time enough for me to secure a handful of cut-price bargains by the Louis Armstrong Hot Five, King Oliver, Bessie Smith, and Muggsy Spanier. Our transactions could afford to be wonderfully affable because we were both getting exactly what we wanted. The new for him, and the old for me. Privately I thought he was mad.

In spite of the family apotheosis of Bunk Johnson, the musical preferences of Honor Oak Park had never been wholly pure, as the records I carried away that evening from my Navarro-worshipping friend indicate. And although my father continued to believe that Bunk was irreplaceable this was because he would have thought it disloyal of him to take any other attitude. It would have meant standing against the musical spirit that had brought light and colour to the otherwise cash-strapped dailiness of our lives. Bunk Johnson was pretty well the only jazz trumpeter he ever referred to by name. If he came into the room while an early jazz record was being playing, something by, say, Tommy Ladnier or King Oliver, he would smile blissfully at the gramophone and mutter 'Dear old Bunk.' The name that could be turned so easily by detractors of revivalism into a cheap jibe was, for him, a general benediction on all traditional jazz.

By the time I was making regular Sunday morning visits to the Centre my musical taste had changed decisively. Topographically, the distance covered wasn't great, but in ideological terms it was vast. In effect, my personal musical odyssey was similar to that undertaken by jazz musicians in 1917 when the American government's closure of Storyville, the red-light district of New Orleans, had accelerated the movement of jazz musicians north to Chicago. We called our kind of jazz after the name of that city. We played Chicago jazz. That meant sidelining Bunk Johnson and George Lewis as our models, and looking instead to Armstrong, Oliver, and Morton. For the purists, it was no less an act of betrayal than pledging our allegiance to someone like, say, Fats Navarro. It could even be regarded as worse than that, a case of being so near and yet so far. And, as we all know, it is there, in distinctions that to outsiders are miniscule and largely irrelevant, that is to be found the true stuff of ideological schisms. *We*, not the modernists – who really couldn't help themselves, poor things – became the purists' enemies.

Chicago jazz. Surely a clear enough indication of the music we were striving to play up at the Centre. But no. Like so many other jazz labels, this one could be treacherous. We followed the Chicago of Armstrong, Oliver, Dodds, and Morton, not the Chicago of Bix Beiderbecke, Bud Freeman, and Eddie Condon. Bix himself was a curious, virtually unique, exception to our normal exclusivity, a white musician from the early days, living among and inspired by the same musicians we adored on record, who had developed his own highly original jazz style without moving too traitorously away from his roots. We approved of him, though we did not treat his successors, Chicagoans who had expanded and popularized Bix's style of Dixieland, with the same liberality. We remained, as it were, on nodding terms with some of them, but no more than that. And we would have nothing at all to do with 'Chicago, Chicago, that toddling town.' Certainly not! That Chicago was placed beside 'The Jazz Singer' and 'The King of Jazz' in our dictionary of dodgy definitions.

We had no doubt in our imaginations about the kind of jazz we wanted to play, but what we were able to produce was restricted by our limited musical abilities and by whatever instrumentation we could manage to assemble. There was no piano in the attic at the Centre and no chance of getting one up there. Although we could manage without it, its absence was of some significance. It was widely argued at the time that true New Orleans jazz should do without a piano, in keeping, presumably, with its marching-band origins. According to this argument, the piano became essential for jazz only because of the commercial corruption of Chicago. Therefore, while it made sense for the purists to dispense with a piano, it was equally reasonable for us to want one. Historically the argument was always a nonsense, except obviously for an actual marching band. A quick look at the line-up of Bunk Johnson's revered New Orleans Jazz Band should have decided that once and for all. Nevertheless, it was a piece of revivalist doctrine that was not easily shaken.

Nor did we have a double bass. There was no disagreement between Chicago and New Orleans on this issue. Every band should have one of them, or, for the purists, a tuba or sousaphone as a more than acceptable substitute. But basses are expensive instruments to buy, difficult to transport, and we didn't know any bass players. Instead we made do with an improvised version constructed from a tea chest, broom handle and piece of string. This ingenious and surprisingly effective alternative, had become closely associated with skiffle and the purists, but for once this didn't worry us. We knew that many early jazz and folk musicians had used such home-made instruments out of financial necessity: it was a valued part of jazz mythology. So although we never were poor in ways that American blacks had been poor, still we were largely working-class teenagers only ten years on from the end of the war, with little money to spend, and improvised musical instruments like tea-chest basses was a taste that Chicago and New Orleans were happy to share.

A drum kit is no easier to transport than a double bass, but it is more adaptable and our drummer, a recruit from my grammar school's army cadet corps, had no difficulty getting a snare drum, cymbal, and some boxes and tins for fancy sound effects up to the attic. He was also an enormously skilful washboard enthusiast. Here was another improvisation claimed by skifflers, but on this solemn matter we took a line of our own, knowing full well that the washboard had appeared on many of the Johnny Dodds small-group records of the 1920s. For us no pedigree could be sounder than that. The rest of our line-up caused few problems. We had a banjo which was especially important to compensate for the absence of a piano; a clarinet, sometimes two; a trombone, only occasionally in the early days, though regularly later on; and the trumpet.

So, there were usually four or five of us. Myself, two school friends, and a couple of outsiders, like our car-owning clarinettist whose enthusiasm for Johnny Dodds we had somehow managed to tap into. This gave us a regular group made up of trumpet, clarinet, drums/washboard, banjo, tea-chest bass, and occasionally trombone. With such a combination, even setting aside our learner status, there was no chance of us fulfilling our ambition to copy the gramophone masterpieces of King Oliver's Creole Jazz Band, Jelly Roll Morton's Red Hot Peppers, and Louis Armstrong's Hot Fives and Sevens. We were, though, able to adapt some of their easier numbers, and we enjoyed the great bonus of there starting to become available on record lots of small-group Chicago jazz, with an instrumentation little different from the only one that we ourselves could put together. Along with Johnny Dodds, we now listened entranced to people like Lovie Austin, Natty Dominique, Tiny Parham, Clarence Williams, Tommy Ladnier and Mezz Mezzrow.

We practised endlessly, tuning in to whatever suitable records we could get hold of, learning individually at home by sitting in, as it were, with the great musicians of the past. None of us could read music, few of us thought it necessary to do so. At the start we were barely aware that different keys existed. Virtually everything we played was in C or F, with an occasional excursion into Eb. We were kept reasonably in tune by the banjo player (or pianist when that luxury was granted us) laying down a tune's basic chord sequence. Small, hand-written notebooks of these sequences were valuable objects. I compiled one of my own and tucked it away in my trumpet case to be ready for any informal session that might crop up. Rehearsing a new number meant the trumpeter or clarinettist learning a melody by ear, and the banjo player working out the chords. Many of these early jazz numbers are not musically demanding – what an Armstrong or Dodds did with them was quite another matter – and we were obliged to turn to the simplest.

We would begin a session with some catchy tunes that were easy to play and popular with all traditionalists such as 'The Sheik of Araby,'

'Ding Dong Daddy,' and 'The World is Waiting for the Sunrise'; then a few easier pieces from Oliver, Armstrong and Morton like 'Canal Street Blues,' 'Dr Jazz,' 'The Last Time,' and 'Muskrat Ramble'; and, most treasured, a number of tunes that became the speciality pieces in our repertoire, 'Travelling Blues,' 'Chicago Buzz,' 'China Boy,' 'Forty and Tight.' The style of music we were striving to capture was tightly organized, crisp, harmonious, technically ambitious, with plenty of room for breaks and solos, hard-driven (something we could hardly avoid with a washboard player as energetic as ours), and 'hot.'

Every Sunday morning and two or three evenings a week, the four or five of us would travel to that remote attic, with its low ceiling, thick wooden beams, and fancy sunshade. The setting was perfect, the atmosphere ideal. The acoustics were close, with the sturdy wood surround absorbing and flattening the sharper noises we produced while at same time allowing the air of intimacy we regarded as the essence of jazz. The sloping windowless roof meant that the only air available to us came up through the ladder's permanently open access panel and was returned by us as hot music, welcome or not as the case may be, to anyone else who happened to be using the Centre.

We told ourselves that we were learning to play our preferred kind of jazz in just the right kind of place. This opinion we reached from a variety of sources, most crucially the central London jazz clubs that we were beginning to visit. Like the attic, they were hot and sweaty, but also crowded with listeners and dancers, an ambition we weren't yet ready even to think of ever achieving. For me the type of jazz club was Cy Laurie's. Everything about it seemed just right, from the atmosphere (shady outside, steamy inside) through to the Johnny Dodds inspired jazz that Cy Laurie recreated. One visit at the age of fifteen or so was enough to turn me into a regular. Cy's, as we always called it, was situated in Windmill Street, on the edge of Soho, just off of Piccadilly Circus, and within easy reach by train from Honor Oak Park. The entrance to the club was a plain wooden door, topped by a small neon sign. Behind the door, a flight of steps led steeply, tantalizingly down to an area shielded from view by a glowing reddish-orange light. It looked wonderfully seedy, but was in truth barely more decadent than the average church youth club. More conventional Soho sleaziness was represented by the notorious Windmill Theatre which stood on the opposite side of the narrow street. The Windmill was still boasting that it had 'never closed,' and as the posters and photographs outside testified it was continuing to feature the statuesque nudes who had been its main contribution to the nation's war effort and the reason why its doors always managed to stay open.

Jazz clubs were also opening up all around us, mainly in the back rooms of pubs. Even the large concert halls in south London were beginning to feature jazz bands, the British pioneers mainly but often supported by lesser-known bands. Our enclosed world was opening up, quickly, excitingly, unbelievably. If we should ever become good enough to move out of the attic there would no shortage of places where we could perform. Meanwhile, our adopted home was fully capable of satisfying our dreams and aspirations. Apart from local developments in the jazz world, we still relied for necessary information on whatever scraps of mythology came our way.

From somewhere or other we learned that the relatively obscure small-group jazz we admired so much and which had been partly dependent as ours was on improvised instruments, had sometimes been called 'rent music,' named, apparently, after the custom of hard-up jazz musicians in America holding informal sessions in their rooms to raise enough money to pay the rent. The phrase might have been coined especially for us, so warmly did we cling to it, so loudly did we proclaim that 'rent music' was what we played. True, we didn't actually have to pay rent at home, at the Centre, or anywhere else, and as yet we couldn't even dream of anyone putting down real money to hear us play whether to raise the rent or not. But the spirit was right. It was all we needed while we were in the attic, our second home, our Chicago, and while the lives and music of American black musicians dating back years before any of us were born, felt more real, more immediate to us than almost anything home grown in the mid-1950s.

* * * *

Self-absorbed though we were, and oblivious to much else around us, we couldn't avoid knowing that we were not the only jazz band with a free right to rehearse at the Centre. Nor were we the first on the scene. We might even, it now occurs to me, have been interlopers, packed off to the attic because the only downstairs space suitable for our kind of activity was already occupied. If so, it was a situation that had worked out well for us and our type of jazz. The quaint cramped setting had given us intimacy, familiarity, and total privacy, apart of course from the open trapdoor. We couldn't have wished for anything better. The alternative, the space that might possibly have been ours if we had arrived a little earlier on the scene, was always on display.

Performing in one of the doorless rooms we had to pass on our way to and from the attic ladder was a New Orleans style band led by a trumpeter who had been to the same school as me. I remembered him being there without knowing him personally. He had been in a higher form and had recently left school entirely. That would have made him a couple of years older than me, seventeen or eighteen to my fifteen or sixteen. He was now working temporarily in an office in central London, filling in time before National Service.

His name was Kenny Croft. He was a purist, and the leader of a band with a classic New Orleans line-up. No piano, definitely by choice in this instance, a real double bass, drums, banjo, trumpet, clarinet and trombone. Surrounding this full complement of musicians was an impressive air of professionalism. For a start, the band had a name – Kenny's own – attached to it. One of the band members, and unsurprisingly so because in those days an exceptionally high proportion of jazz musicians were also artists or cartoonists or art students of one kind or another, had designed a billboard, a two-sided free-standing structure of the kind commonly seen outside newsagents' shops. This was always placed beside the band during rehearsals. Painted on the board, in elegant white letters set against a deep red background, were the words, The Kenny Croft New Orleans Jazzmen.

The band was able to draw on the services of a crumpled old van that was covered with dents and buckles and clattered and clanged noisily whenever it was asked to move. It was owned, driven, and maintained by the drummer. Although this was a time when there were far more old than new cars on London's roads, there was a rather special fragility about this particular van. Still, rickety it may have been but it was good enough to do what was asked of it which was to transport all of the band and their instruments wherever they wanted to go. Two band members would squeeze onto the single front seat next to the driver, leaving the remaining three to squat on the floor in the back with the instruments piled around and over them. It wasn't possible to travel very far in this manner, but for the moment, that didn't matter.

The van was needed because the Kenny Croft's New Orleans Jazzmen were beginning to be offered the occasional paid gig, usually filling the intervals at small jazz clubs, most of them nearby. The band was paid as much as five or six pounds a time. Once the cost of petrol was deducted, the musicians could make something like ten or fifteen shillings each, say 75p in today's money. So far the nearest we had got to that kind of prestige was inflicting our unpaid attention on friends at a local church youth club for a short spell in an evening devoted otherwise to ball-room dancing to gramophone records.

I don't think we were envious of the success that was starting to come to Kenny's band. Not consciously anyway. We made fun of them, but in those days there wasn't much that we didn't make fun of, apart from the two sacred subjects of our own – traditional jazz and literature. But the true reason why we treated them with mockery rather than envy was that we didn't think the music they played was worth bothering about. There was also an unspoken understanding that we were all on the same kind of amateur career path. What to us seemed pretentious in Kenny's set-up were precisely the fairly mundane things that we ourselves were so far incapable of achieving, things that we were cockily sure would sooner or later come our way as well. We were simply a few years younger than them. That's all it was. As we continued to practise and improve, we too would be offered paid gigs, obtain a proper bass player and pianist, and a van to carry us about. This was the way traditional jazz was going.

Kenny was not only older and more advanced professionally than the rest of us, he was also taller, by as much as three or four inches. And he was thin, skinny rather, with a tight peaky face, long nose and prominent Adam's apple. He had very dark short hair that was neatly greased. For many years I imagined him as always wearing our school uniform which consisted of a navy blue blazer, grey flannels, black shoes, white shirt, and a blue and white striped tie, the only changes being that he had discarded the blazer and replaced the tie with something even plainer. That is how I remember first seeing him at the Centre, but I can't possibly have been right. I now think there must have been a bit more to this business of Kenny's clothes.

All of us connected with jazz (whether Trads, Purists, or Mods) tended to wear clothes which announced our musical allegiances. Trads and Purists inclined to duffle coats, corduroy trousers and heavy sweaters: Mods to tight-fitting Italian suits, button-down American shirts, and slim ties. Kenny followed neither of these trends, though he did dress in a representative manner, maintaining a simple code of neatness that was intended to express his unconditional devotion to the spirit of New Orleans. With his school blazer removed, a simple black tie, shirt sleeves rolled down and buttoned at the wrists, charcoal grey trousers and shiny black shoes, he would have had no difficulty passing for a member of one of the New Orleans marching bands that no doubt occupied his most intimate dreams, nightly and daily. It was an intense imaginative experience that I should really have recognized much earlier than I did. After all, participating in a New Orleans style funeral was a fantasy shared by all of us.

If a member of one of our families had died, we would have had little idea how their mortal remains were to be disposed of. We knew, of course, that they would be buried in one of the many cemeteries that surrounded our homes in South London. A particularly large and impressive example was situated not far from the Centre We were also familiar enough with the reality of death. In very poor families like mine, adults were obliged to struggle from a relatively early age with illnesses that were debilitating at best, and often terminal. This necessary air of acceptance carried with it a rigid adherence to public rituals. Whenever a funeral cortège passed us in the street, my father would stop whatever he was doing, remove his cap, and stand still until the big black cars had disappeared. We children were taught to behave in the same respectful manner. At the same time, we were protected or distanced from death.

As a younger generation already preparing to act our parts in an iconoclastic age, and especially those of us who clung so passionately to jazz as a way of life, we were increasingly aware that these public codes associated with death and burial had little to do with our own emotions and feelings. In my family there was no established pattern of churchgoing and the younger children rarely attended a family funeral. The whole business was an unrevealed mystery to us, the large black cars, bigger and posher than anything we knew in everyday life; the dressing up in best suits or the buying of otherwise unaffordable clothes especially for the event; the processing solemnly in and out of a church, and finally on to the graveside. What annoyed us was that it was systematically, formally, boringly, and, unforgivably, carried out with the wrong accompanying music.

We were sure of this because if we had been transported bodily to New Orleans, our 'land of dreams,' where our imaginations already dwelt for much of the time, we would have had no difficulty understanding what was going on or even organizing the programme. We were up to rambling with the best of them. Slowly, mournfully, wailingly on the way to the burial place, with the band playing 'Flee as a Bird'; humbly, silently by the grave while the dead body was lowered into it, heads bowed and musical instruments lowered to the ground in symbolic burial as the preacher intoned 'Ashes to Ashes and Dust to Dust'; and then joyfully back home, swaying in time to 'Oh Didn't he Ramble.' This would be in march tempo at first, but freed up as soon as the graveyard faded in the distance behind us. Then we would dance our way to the local hall to play and gyrate throughout the night to rags and stomps and blues. We knew all about it. That was the way, the approved way, the only possible way to go.

We knew from photographs exactly how those marching-band musicians looked. They wore smart white shirts, black ties, trousers and shoes, and peaked caps. In fact, just like Kenny as we observed him every Sunday morning fronting his jazzmen in at the Centre. Even the cap? Well, I have to admit that he wouldn't have worn it at school or in the streets, and I honestly wouldn't be able to stand up in court and swear to ever having known him wear one at all. But I have a strong fancy that on at least one occasion I caught a glimpse of him in their large airy room leading his band into the twentieth or thirtieth chorus of 'Lord, Lord, Lord' or 'Postman's Lament,' dressed in his marching-band uniform, with a peaked cap fixed jauntily on his head. I like to think I did, anyway.

What he lacked was the joyfulness of body and spirit that those American musicians conveyed so convincingly even in a faded photograph. Kenny was the English version, circa 1955. He looked austere, taking his pleasures very seriously indeed, his lank body in harmony with the statutory mood of personal dedication to the Crescent City. He was closer to those black-garbed, seventeenth-century Puritans who were deemed to be insufficiently of this world to receive earthly names. Instead they were labelled with moral qualities which they were then obliged to carry with them through life. At their simplest, Charity, Faith or Verity, and with a bit more self-conscious elaboration, Harmony-with-Jesus, Faithful-unto-Death, Steadfastness-in-the-name-of-the Lord. That kind of thing.

All of these devotional qualities applied to Kenny, and his Lord could be found most nights of the week, playing the trumpet in a subterranean jazz club in Great Newport Street, very near Leicester Square, in London's West End. He was called Ken Colyer, and goodness, was Kenny faithful unto him. No seventeenth-century Puritan could ever have been more steadfast in the ways of the Lord than Kenny Croft was in his.

That Colyer qualified at all for this kind of treatment was itself anomalous, a weird reversal of everything we would normally have regarded as authentic. Nothing about him was right, theoretically at least: not his colour, birthplace or upbringing. Aged, at that time I suppose, in his early thirties, he was the active leader of the purest of the pure revivalist bands, and although we tended to make fun of him, and of Kenny too for being one of his disciples, we all believed that Colyer was the genuine article and fully deserved his legendary status, even though he was white, English, and had been born in Great Yarmouth.

Like most traditionalists, high or low, pure or impure, Colyer had formed his musical opinions about jazz, and had learned to play the cornet, from gramophone records, especially, in his case, those of the Bunk Johnson and George Lewis bands. Together with some fellow enthusiasts in London he had tried to recreate the sounds he was hearing on records. But after a short while he decided to search out the real thing, and why not? After all, some at least of the musicians he most admired were, thanks to the revivalist activity of the 1940s, still alive and performing. This was the simple profound moment of understanding that Colyer acted on. He packed his cornet, joined the merchant navy, jumped ship at the first port of call in America, and headed for New Orleans. There, until he was deported by the immigration authorities, he spent his time playing the real music with real musicians and absorbing the purist creed that would stay with him undimmed for the rest of his life.

He returned home to be welcomed as leader of a band that was in the process of being formed by clarinettist Monty Sunshine and trombonist Chris Barber. They were already familiar figures in the traditional jazz world. Sunshine had played with Colyer before the trip to New Orleans in the English revivalist band The Crane River Jazz Band, while Barber had fronted his own band modelled on the King Oliver Creole Jazz Band. Any personal ambitions Sunshine and Barber might have had were offered up as a tribute to Colyer's more adventurous spirit. For a while they were all in musical and ideological harmony, and then suddenly fell out with each other. No sound could ever be quite right for Colyer, no band was ever stable. Obsessively set on a quest to recreate the music he had experienced in New Orleans, his future career was to be one of constant quarrels with other musicians and frequent changes of band personnel. The object of his quest was pretty well unattainable. It would have been easier for him if he had been striving for something new and different. But he was searching for something old and the same. He didn't want to change anything. He wanted to unchange things.

Whatever the truth of his split with Sunshine and Barber, the division itself fairly represented the fundamental differences in British traditional jazz between its pure and its impure varieties. Once again, the language of old-time religion is best fitted to express the feelings at stake. In affirming so resolutely that this way was right and that wrong, Colyer crystallized attitudes and sanctified martyrdom. We were never to know for sure whether Colyer sacked all the other members of the band or they sacked him, but under Chris Barber's leadership and an inexperienced Pat Halcox taking over from Colyer on trumpet the same group of musicians were soon producing their own distinctive traditional jazz sound and becoming, in the process, a huge popular success. Colyer stayed put, insisting on fidelity to an ideal, the original exponents of which were now rapidly dying out. No doubt he made a decent enough living in the process, even if he was never what could be called popular. But if he had, that would have involved what he himself condemned in others as selling out to commercialism and he was determined to hold aloof.

Kenny Croft was a disciple of both Colyer and the musicians of whom Colyer was himself a disciple. That meant, immediately, Bunk Johnson but also the various bands, most of them led by George Lewis, which had proliferated since Bunk's death. Kenny's band at the Centre was pastiche Colyer, just as, we said endlessly and scornfully, Colyer's band was pastiche Lewis. Fundamentally they weren't behaving any differently from us up in the attic. They were simply following different models, though this was something we refused to understand.

At the heart of the repertoire of Kenny's band were some dozen or so New Orleans spirituals such as 'Lord, Lord, Lord,' 'Sing On,' and 'Oh for a Closer Walk with Thee.' Linked culturally with these, though musically more ambitious, were a handful of New Orleans street marches, notably 'Salutation March,' and 'Moose March'; a number of twelve-bar blues like 'Easy Rider'; and a range of once-popular songs which had been given revivalist respectability by Bunk, and, in turn, by Colyer himself. 'Oh, you beautiful Doll' was a great favourite, along with others such as 'Tiptoe through the Tulips' and 'Till we meet Again.' Now and then we could also hear drifting faintly through the Centre Kenny and his jazzmen struggling bravely with some of the more complex, orchestrated ragtime numbers which both the Colyer and Barber bands, following Bunk's example, played so well.

Most of these tunes were given the same treatment. Chorus after chorus of ensemble. Twenty, thirty, fifty, who knows? As many, we supposed, as Kenny's breath could sustain. Although slight variations were added to the basic melody, nothing was allowed that might be construed as unorthodox. Solos were taken only occasionally. Where breaks by individual instruments were traditional, which meant being sanctified by the recorded model, they were acknowledged and either copied from the original or given some individual variation, the situation here being similar to the attitudes of classical musicians to cadenzas. When called for, Kenny himself would take the vocals in the approved Ken Colyer manner, with trumpet tucked under one arm, leaving the hands free to clap in rhythm. Even prejudice as strong as ours had to acknowledge that Colyer had an attractive singing voice. It was soft, with a slight burr, surprisingly English with merely a trace of what for the rest of us was an obligatory American emphasis, and creating a melodic effect that was intimate, confidential.

It was this distinctive manner of Ken's that Kenny imitated with some success, caressing his favourite spirituals and hymns with a nasal mid-Atlantic drawl:

> Lord, Lord, Lord, Lord,
> You've sure been good to me.
>
> Lord, Lord, Lord Lord,
> You've sure been good to me.
>
> Oh the Lord's been good to me.

It was performances such as these that set us most apart from the Kenny Croft New Orleans Jazzmen, and not simply because of the vocals and the endless repetition. More significant was the tricky question of religion.

As good Chicagoans we had largely dispensed with the spirituals and gospels that we accepted were always present in jazz, though, for us peripherally so. When our heroes had moved north from the Crescent City to the Windy City they appeared to have left behind them most of the church-based communal experiences that had been so influential on their music. Once in Chicago they most certainly did not wander the streets chanting 'Lord, Lord, Lord' and 'Sing On, Sing On, Sing On.' They were more likely to wear snazzy expensive clothes and perform lightly orchestrated arrangements on elegant bandstands in fancy ballrooms. But Kenny wasn't for leaving anything behind.

Not only did he treasure every scrap of black spirituality, he expressed it with such feeling that it might have been the faith into which he had been born and which had nurtured and formed him. There was no self-consciousness or embarrassment. What could it possibly matter that this was London in 1955, not New Orleans fifty years earlier? Nothing at all, that's the answer. Everything was taken on board. The purists were happy-clappies long before the phrase, and the attitudes associated with it, conquered the centres of established religion in Britain:

> Sing Hallelujah, I'm walking with the King,
>   Walking with the King, walking with the King.
> Sing Hallelujah, I'm walking with the King,
>   Every day I'm walking with the King.

This would have been Kenny in confident mode. More often he would be desperately, mournfully, yearning for the Lord's protection:

> Just a closer walk with Thee,
>   Grant it Jesus if you please,
> I'll be walking close with thee,
>   Let it be, dear Lord, let it be.

Spiritual comfort was necessary because of the never-ending labour of daily life:

> My day is hot and long,
>> I trudge and sing this song,
> Oh Lord take this sack from my back.

The only earthly delight, other than that provided by the eventual certainty of walking with the King, was the knowledge that in the fullness of time everything must come to an end. On that glorious day, the agonizing pain would cease as the burden of life fell away:

> Down by the riverside I'm gonna lay my burden down,
> Down by the riverside I'm gonna lay my burden down.

The certainty of release was eased by the knowledge that life itself was nothing to boast about or even value. At best it was made up entirely of pain and labour, imposed by either the inherently sinful nature of man or the harsh social conditions in which he was forced to live, with his agony being eased only by the realization that life was thankfully short:

> Just a little while to stay here,
> Just a little while to wait,
> Just a little while to labour...

Kenny always succeeded in making it sound as though he was the most burdened sinner in the Western world since Bunyan's Christian, and that, like Christian, the burden of life would only be lifted from him if he succeeded in trudging faithfully on to the Celestial City.

In their own manner all of these songs were optimistic in that they were based in the conviction of a sure and certain salvation. The temptation was always there to take control for oneself and end the misery, or to 'jump off the bridge and drown' as the mournful postman in his pathetic lament considers doing, but it was rare for there not to be present a hope that when that sweet day of death does arrive the Lord will be there to comfort and protect. And not just at the moment of death. He is life's constant companion, the only one it is possible to trust:

> Nobody knows the trouble I've seen,
> Nobody knows but Jesus.

However sad the end, its transformation into joy is certain. This is the moment that the whole of life has been leading up to, the moment when you join the Saints and go marching with them through the pearly gates confident that Jesus will be there waiting for you.

Kenny reserved his deepest passion for the funeral march 'Didn't he Ramble' which always received the full treatment: chants, shouts, wails, graveside mourning, the lot! Sometimes, up in the attic on a Sunday morning, while energetically rehearsing our own numbers, we would hear his plaintive call rise up to us through the trapdoor: 'Oh, Didn't he ramble! Didn't he ramble!' while the massed voices of his jazzmen would respond with, 'Oh yes, he rambled, he rambled. He rambled, till the butchers cut him down.'

All of the band followed their leader in dressing neatly, adding their choral voices (and clapping hands) to his vocals, and taking care to see that their handsome billboard was always prominently displayed, even for what we would have regarded as a casual rehearsal at the Centre. Propped in front of Kenny and his trombonist there were metal stands, adjusted to a height suitable for the relevant instrument, with shiny silver bowler hats clipped to them. These were used to create the hollow echoing sound which was so valued by purists and which was greatly enhanced by the Centre's large empty spaces.

Along with the other qualities Kenny had taken over from his great hero was the tone of Colyer's trumpet playing, and that, we all agreed, was taking things one very big step too far. How best to describe the tone of Colyer's playing was a topic of much humorous comment among us. What was the best word for it? Whole paragraphs of Roget's *Thesaurus* would have been incapable of coming up with an adjective that everyone could have agreed on. Weak, thin, wavering (or quavering), whining, shaky, stuttering, wailing, faltering. It wasn't hot and brilliant like Louis or sweet and rounded like Bunk or silvery like Bix, but rather, as everyone except Colyer's most committed disciples acknowledged, thin, puny, scrawny even. And Kenny Croft had succeeded in copying it to perfection.

As, of course, he would be expected to. What was there of Kenny that didn't come from Ken? Nothing. The matter of the similar sounding names and the identical initials couldn't possibly be simply a coincidence. We decided that there had to be spookier connections. As we possessed no reliable information on such matters, we happily made up our own, aggressively self-confident in our rootless, jokey grammar-school manner. For a while, influenced by a now forgotten literary source, probably Robert Graves whose mythological writings were a preoccupation of our washboard player, we decided that Kenny Croft had not been born in the normal way but must have sprung fully formed from the head of his spiritual father Ken Colyer just as Athene was reputed to have done from the head of her father Zeus.

After a while that was changed into a romantic tale that involved Kenny, a foundling, a long skinny baby, dressed only in a black tie and a miniature peaked cap perched on his little head, a trumpet longer than himself by his side and a notice round his neck reading KC, being deposited at dead of night on the doorstep of a childless London couple. That we also eventually surrendered, finally deciding that there was nothing truly mysterious about his family background. It was simply that he hadn't originally been christened Kenny (or Ken or Kenneth) at all, but had changed his name by deed poll once he discovered his true destiny in life. Perhaps his parents had bought him his new name, together with a trumpet, as a birthday present.

Strained our fables may have been, and a good bit too self-consciously literary as well, but they were necessary to our own comfort. We couldn't possibly rest satisfied with the explanation that Kenny was simply copying Ken Colyer who was copying Bunk Johnson and George Lewis exactly as we were copying Louis Armstrong and Johnny Dodds. Kenny was the cracked mirror that reflected much of our own image all too faithfully back upon us, and distorted the rest. His kind of music we could enjoy well enough, though it often suited us to act as though it was unbearable to us. The religious attitudes that came with the music and which made him behave as though he was a reincarnated cotton-picking slave we treated with derision.

Still, try as we did to separate ourselves from Kenny by mocking him, we were just as immersed as he was in a way of life that was personally foreign to us; just as sympathetic to those remarkable early musicians in New Orleans who had created bewilderingly original music in spite of, or out of, their desperately hard lives; just as eager to surrender our souls to this new religion which was such a welcome replacement for the old; and just as determined to search out and isolate the heretical among us. We dealt with any threat Kenny posed us by providing him with a mock-heroic status in the pantheon of jazz legends. Our satire we felt to be justified because the God he was worshipping was so obviously false. Choosing one style rather than another couldn't possibly be explained away as a matter of personal taste, not for us or for him. Kenny hadn't taken a wrong path, he had taken *no* path at all. We, of course had behaved far more positively, moving on to Chicago, ready to learn and expand and develop. But Kenny was regressive, we decided, using with relish a word we had recently discovered. He had stayed where he was in New Orleans, but a New Orleans that was based not in Louisiana but in London's West End.

The differences between our two bands were not communicated in any direct manner, friendly or otherwise, and with Kenny himself I can't remember ever having a sustained conversation. An exchange between us that was not ironic would have been rendered impossible by the rigidity of our respective positions. What was there to say to each other that could rise above our engrained disapproval? If Kenny's band was already playing when we arrived at the Centre we might offer a wordless ironic wave of greeting as we passed the open door or hurl through it the gently abusive words 'Mouldy Fig.' Nobody wholeheartedly committed to New Orleans liked to hear that particular label because it was coined for them alone. Not that we had the faintest idea where it came from or what exactly it meant. I'm not sure that I do even now. It was apt and fair comment. That was all we cared about, as we strolled through primitive New Orleans and climbed our ladder to relatively sophisticated Chicago, leaving mouldy figdom far below us.

Kenny

'See you at Cy's,' was our regular jaunty greeting to Kenny if we happened to pass him in the street or bump into him as he was leaving the Centre. He would smile sadly and shake his head at us.

By this time Cy Laurie's had become established as our model of jazz-club authenticity. Kenny's exact equivalent was Ken Colyer's. The two clubs were no more than ten minutes walk from each other, one on either side of Soho. For us they served as essential boundary markers, with Shaftesbury Avenue the major thoroughfare between them. There was even a challenging alternative. By turning direct north and walking through Soho you could reach 100 Oxford Street, the final major venue of the London trilogy of trad temples. This was where Humphrey Lyttleton and a number of other less musically narrow British trad bands presided. Our invitation to Kenny to join us at Cy's was, of course, a taunt, and a good one. We knew it was as impossible for him to make the ten minute stroll from the centre of purity at Ken Colyer's to Cy Laurie's heretical stronghold, as it would have been for us to travel the same distance in the opposite direction. And none of us would ever meet up at 100 Oxford Street. Oh goodness no!

Even here we maintained the barriers that determined our behaviour at school and the Centre. Nothing was allowed to break our adherence to one or other side of the great divide. There was no give, no take. We had been presented with a music that we knew to be the most important of the age. A music that gave new meaning to life, that was in itself a way of life. And once it became ours, we immediately behaved as unyielding sectarians tend to do. We divided up our property, winnowing out the true from the false, separating apostates from believers, keeping well apart from each other, making sure there was no way for corruption to get through to us.

* * * *

Early one December, at school assembly, the headmaster opened proceedings by telling us in a solemn tone that he had an announcement to make and would we all be sure to remain in the hall and *not* rush off as soon as the morning hymn was over.

The weather that winter had been terrible, day after day of heavy fog, filthier and nastier than usual, a ground-level, enveloping cloud of yellow poison that followed you along the streets, wrapping itself insidiously around you, fingering your neck and hair. Virtually every aspect of our lives was affected by it. At home, the fog made it all but impossible for my father to get through the front door of an evening before collapsing into a kitchen chair, gasping to cough up and spit on the fire the clotted phlegm, itself the same colours as the polluted air surrounding all of us, that filled his lungs as he struggled to get back from work. After one of these attacks he would sit hunched at the dinner table, barely touching the hot meal which my mother always had waiting ready for him. Arriving home at all was a victory. In just this kind of weather he had once taken refuge in the doorway of a closed shop some fifty yards from our house. There he had been forced to remain, bent double, his arms clamped tightly round his body, for an hour before he could find the amount of breath needed to complete the short distance left of his journey home.

I was young and fit enough, and too obsessively anticipating the next session, ever to have allowed the fog to be so dense as to prevent me, awkward trumpet case and all, from walking to the Centre. Even so, weather as bad as this would disrupt our sessions. It was unthinkable for our clarinettist to drive across a south London where visibility on the roads had all but ceased to exist. We were always being reminded by those with long memories that public transport wouldn't have been disrupted in this way by fog if the trams hadn't been removed. But they had, and free-running modern traffic couldn't cope in the same way. The fog made life difficult for everyone. It was on such a day that the headmaster who, as we all knew was himself unable to get home in such weather and used to sleep in a little bedroom next to his office, told us he had an important announcement to make.

We were standing packed together in the school hall, restless as usual and with many of us on this particular day wet and uncomfortable as well from having been forced to walk to school. The daily hymn was sung with its customary air of joylessness, and while we waited to hear what the headmaster had to say, we fidgeted and shuffled, interested only in breaking away quickly into smaller groups of friends. He spoke first of the dreadful weather we had endured for some days past and how everyone was inconvenienced by it. But for some of us it had involved far more than a local inconvenience. He had just learned of a road accident two days earlier in which a former pupil of the school had been tragically killed. His name was Kenneth Croft, and he had been a schoolboy here until three years ago.

Perhaps only a few of you, he suggested ruminatively, emotionally, would have known him personally. Schools are like that. Boys come and go, stay for a short time, move on, and only ever become known to a small portion of their fellow schoolboys. But nevertheless, until recently Kenneth Croft *had* been one of our community, and his interests although by no means shared by everybody were deep and sincere. While still at school he had formed a jazz band. Jazz was a great passion with him, and over the past year or so he had started to build a career for himself as a jazz musician. His shocking death was connected with this great love of his. The band had been on the way to an engagement in the fog when a car had crashed into the side of the van in which they were travelling. Kenneth, apparently, had been in the front seat, at the point where the car collided. He was the only one killed. The other members of the band were not seriously harmed.

The head explained that he had no further details of the accident, his sole purpose that morning being to draw our attention to this unhappy event. The lesson he wanted us to take from it was that Kenneth Croft had stood where we were standing now. He had joined in the hymn singing and listened to the lesson being read, as we had just done. He had gone to classes, played rugby and cricket, done his homework, and taken his part in the same routine as us. Now this shocking accident had removed him from life. We should try to think on such things. The sympathy of the whole school, staff and pupils, would be conveyed to his parents, and there would now be a moment of silence for us all to be respectful to Kenneth's memory and to the life that has been taken from us.

Apart from that enforced minute I can't be sure that those of us who were connected with the Centre managed any respectful silence of our own. I don't remember us being silent at all, and I very much doubt if we were. In fact, I think it unlikely we managed to cover the distance from the school hall to our first class of the day without bursting into laughter. It was just about the funniest thing we had ever heard. The jokes began immediately.

Kenny dead and gone to glory! And the cause of it that shabby old tin van that he had been so proud to flaunt at the Centre. Who'd have believed it? Kenny's burden finally lifted, his daily toils over, his worries gone for ever. No longer would he suffer alone. From now and for ever onward he really would be marching with the King. He had been summoned by Gabriel who must have decided that his heavenly band could no longer manage without a second horn. Goodness, just imagine the scene when those two got together. What a session that would be! Week after week we had heard Kenny calling for the Saints to go marching in and now he had joined them, cakewalking and strutting, playing his part in the great marching band in the sky, ready and eager for those pearly gates to open up for him.

In the usual literary manner of which we were so proud, one or other of us took the trouble to check the word Saints in the large dictionary housed in a nearby public library reading room, another building with free access that played a huge part in our everyday lives. Saints might have been considered a simple enough word for us to understand, but the iconic churchy figures it conjured up didn't quite fit in with the jazz scene we knew so well. The dictionary was helpful. It informed us that a Saint is someone who after death is given an exalted place in heaven and treated with veneration by God. Collectively, we learned, 'the Saints' were a body of persons who were 'righteous in God's sight.'

What information could be better for Kenny than that? He was exalted (or always thought he was) and righteous (or at least self-righteous), no one more so when purity was the issue. That he had been called so early probably meant that God had been keeping an eye on him. That bothered us a bit. We didn't like to suggest that God was capable of making a mistake, but everything didn't quite fit together. For the purposes of the heavenly marching band, it must surely have been Gabriel, not God, who was in charge of musical arrangements. After all, anyone who would allow Kenny's tinny Ken Colyer inspired vibrato into one of his sessions would have to be more than a little tone deaf. Perhaps he wouldn't let Kenny join his band straight away. He would almost certainly insist on a bit of extra tuition first. A crash course of listening to some records by the Hot Five and the Red Hot Peppers seemed a likely possibility. 'You'll have to go easy on the Mouldy Fig,' Gabriel was probably advising Kenny at this very moment. 'And on the ensembles as well. Standing shoulder to shoulder, back to back, one for all and that kind of thing is a virtue, of course, but there are moments in life when you can have too much of it, and jazz is one of those moments.'

It was all so extraordinarily the most perfectly appropriate event any of us could have imagined, making of life and death a complete harmony. Every Sunday morning Kenny had freed his imagination, his soul, his everyday life even, of its south London context, and in the Centre, with his trusty jazzmen gathered around him, had rehearsed over and over again the New Orleans funeral parade of which he had now so unexpectedly become the focal point. 'Ask not for whom the bell tolls ' we muttered to each other knowingly, as familiar with John Donne and Ernest Hemingway as with Louis Armstrong and Johnny Dodds. There was no need to bother with an answer, not in this case. It was Kenny's soul that was being tolled for. The mourning host was gathering. Rehearsal was now having to make way for the real thing. All those Sunday morning efforts were to be tested in the most poetic, the most ironic, or (who knows?), in the most practical of ways:

> Oh didn't he ramble, didn't he ramble,
> He rambled till the butchers cut him down.

Once laid low and death acknowledged, we all understood – Kenny as well as any of us – that mourning should not be prolonged unnecessarily, but cease once the troubling breath of life has finally departed the body. It was the code we all yearned to live by, its key elements shouted out by

Kenny at the Centre every Sunday morning, with us responding in the prescribed manner, calling back down the attic ladder, 'Yea, oh yea. He rambled, he rambled, till the butchers cut him down.' It was life as we all wanted it to be, even if, as yet, it involved experiences of which we had only musical knowledge:

> Ashes to ashes, dust to dust,
> If the whisky don't get you, the women must.

From that moment at the graveside, with the inevitability of death settled in the only way we knew, the music must be allowed to take over. There would be the foot-dragging march to the burial place, the releasing of the soul ('Flee as the Bird'), and then back home to dance and stomp the night away, glorying in the ways of the Lord.

In our more reflective moments we wondered whether Kenny's family would try to acknowledge his specialness in a suitable manner. However misguided he may have been, his devotion to jazz ought to be publicly recognized. Had the rest of the band gone to play at his graveside? Did his parents bury his trumpet with him? We decided that any such gestures were as unlikely to come from his parents as they would be to come from ours. Jazz was *our* musical language not theirs. I was certain that if it had been my funeral taking place, even someone as relatively liberated in the sounds of jazz as my father wouldn't have hired a New Orleans style band to play at my funeral. As for Kenny's family, well, the truth was we knew as little about them as we did about Kenny himself. We couldn't even be sure he had a family, let alone how the individual members of it might or might not respond to such delicate matters.

Nor did we, it very quickly became apparent, know anything about his fellow jazzmen. Not their individual names or where they came from or how they got together or how they existed when they weren't playing echoing chorus after echoing chorus of 'Sing On' and 'Lord Lord Lord.' To us they hadn't really been people at all, simply a Sunday morning sound, copied from records, personally invigorated by Kenny on his return from his Saturday night pilgrimages to Ken Colyer's. And what a sound it had been! Something to pass by with a laugh and a bit of hard-hearted sarcasm on the way to our attic heaven. We had always wanted Kenny Croft's New Orleans Jazzmen to be simply a false noise, and now they could never be anything else.

On our Sunday morning visits to the Centre after we had learned of Kenny's death we were foolishly surprised to find his old room empty and silent. I suppose we hadn't been capable of believing that any personal tragedy was big enough to prevent the show from going on. But there was no ceremony, no mourning, no grief, no jazzmen anywhere around. Just emptiness. The whole band had melted away with Kenny himself. Someone must have come along and collected the bowler hats, the metal stands, the billboard, and any other props. We shrugged off any feeling of ghostliness the empty space provoked in us, assuming that it could only possibly be a temporary break. They would return next week, or the week after that, or sometime soon. How could they stay away? They were probably arranging auditions to find a new trumpet player.

But if the other members of the band were regrouping, the Centre didn't figure in their plans. We never saw or heard of any of them ever again. We went on climbing our ladder and playing our neat little arrangements of 'Forty and Tight,' 'China Boy' and 'Papa Dip.' We felt we were getting better all the time. The endless rehearsals were beginning to pay off. New musicians were turning up and joining in, enlarging the group and encouraging more invitations to play at the local youth club. We even started allowing into our attic sessions a few non-players; friends from school or girls we had begun to see regularly. These special guests were permitted to sit around on the wooden floor, to listen, admire, and contribute a bit of much needed atmosphere.

I don't think we went on playing at the Centre for much longer, though I can't be sure whether we did or not because it's here that my memory starts to give out. The truth is, after Kenny's death I don't remember us playing at the Centre at all, and I suppose the reason why I can't separate the two experiences is because over the years my memories of the place have become indistinguishable from my memories of him. Why else should it be that the rooms at the Centre and the sounds produced in them should carry clearly through time while the surrounding streets I walked along so happily two or three times a week for a period of some eighteen months, are transformed into an impenetrable suburban forest? It's now impossible for me to remember the Centre without remembering Kenny, and he's not there, and hasn't been for a very long time. It's not easy to lay down street directions how to reach someone who doesn't exist.

Still, reason insists that we must have continued playing at the Centre for a bit longer. After all, it was only Kenny who had disappeared so absolutely. The music, and the spaces, and the different sounds made within them still existed, and so did the ideals, divisions, and separations. Kenny's death had not affected any of this. Nor was it responsible for us eventually leaving the Centre behind. That was simply part of the natural order of things, at least for those of us who Fate had generously allowed to move on. Our lives were changing, we were growing up, and the specialness of our jazz-dominated world was being challenged by priorities that were no different from those affecting everyone else around us. We left school, or took jobs, or started to think of this or that girl as being rather different from the rest, or came under new influences, or quarrelled with and parted from friends, or registered for National Service or university.

For a while Kenny had been for us the type of false choice, the way we shouldn't even think of going, a wrong musical turning, and therefore, because we had made the right choice, a necessary butt of our adolescent ridicule. When he vanished there were only the jokes, and they had very little staying power. All that Kenny's death could possibly mean to us at the time was a stylistic victory in a conflict that had been not unlike the 'cutting contests' we had read about so avidly in which rival bands confronted each other on the streets of New Orleans and fought it out musically until one or other of them retreated, 'cut' to pieces.

There could only ever be one King at a time, of New Orleans or anywhere else. Even though we ourselves hadn't blown Kenny out of public consideration, which was traditionally the aim of a cutting contest, we had enjoyed a victory of sorts, of our taste over his, our minds over his body. We celebrated our triumph with our usual self-conscious literary humour, made votive offerings to the community of saints and archangels with whom Kenny would now be dwelling, and carried on much as before.

* * * *

Becoming a professional jazz musician had never been a serious ambition for me. A fleeting adolescent dream but nothing more substantial than that. Even so, for ten years or so playing the trumpet dominated my life. The instrument itself was a steady companion, carried to the unlikeliest places at the strangest times of day and night on the off chance that I might bump into other enthusiasts and get involved in a session. No opportunity to play was ever willingly passed up, but there was no wish on my part to turn a part-time passion into a full-time occupation. I knew I was never going to be good enough to earn a living as a jazz musician, though there must have been more to it than simply that. After all, if professionalism had been my aim I could have worked harder to improve my playing, studied the instrument more thoroughly, extended my always limited range and control, and have learned to read music.

I refused stubbornly to do any of these things but remained content with getting by as I was. Nor was playing the trumpet ever a totally engrossing interest. It was always shared with books, the two happily dividing my attention, fully compatible, not in competition with each other. Although I had never considered the possibility of having to choose between them, I must have known that if such a moment should ever arise, books would win.

Buried deeply inside me was the conviction that as far as playing the trumpet was concerned, amateur status was the only one I wanted to claim. All those teenage concerns with pure and impure forms of jazz; with selling out or holding on; with living by one's convictions, however misinformed they may have been, had taken root. They underpinned a romantic idealism that for reasons I have never been able to understand developed in me at a very early age. In the case of jazz it shaped itself as a determination to preserve the essence of something that had been so completely a part of my life, rough and ready though in many ways it was, rather than risk allowing professionalism to transform it into something different. There are many ways of following a dream, and this was mine.

As it happened, extraordinary good luck intervened to feed my romanticism and at the same time abolish for ever the possibility that I would ever regret clinging to amateurism. For a few years, in the late 1950s and the early 1960s, the traditional jazz market in Britain found itself in the hitherto inconceivable position of becoming affiliated to the rapidly booming teenage pop industry. The sudden popularity of Trad, as it quickly came to be called, made the outcast state we had been so proud of seem rather quaint. Without any planning or scheming on anyone's part, it suddenly became possible for traditional jazz musicians to keep their principles intact (or throw them overboard), continue to play as and how they pleased (or in ways that satisfied their new pop public), and to perform according to whatever ability they were capable of (or whatever standard they could get away with).

This, it seemed, was what all those hours spent playing along with gramophone records and rehearsing at the Centre had been about. Traditional jazz musicians who were keen to devote themselves fully to playing found that it was now feasible for them to give up their day jobs and concentrate on selling whatever talent they had in the market place. For all but the very humblest, there were agents eager to organize bookings, arrange regular gigs for the band, and take their ten per cent from everything earned. Newly professional bands were now offered opportunities to spend a few months playing in Germany or Holland, tour the cellars and pub back rooms of Britain's provincial towns, appear on the new television pop shows, and, most astonishing of all, to make something like a reasonable living from it.

For those of us who for one reason or another weren't drawn to such options, public demand was sufficiently buoyant to support a form of semi-professionalism which allowed us to maintain our day jobs and take to the road in the evening. This way we could continue playing jazz with old and new friends and while doing so earn enough to pay the cost of petrol, beer and cigarettes, with perhaps a little bit over. It wasn't difficult to tell ourselves that this was what jazz should be all about, and, properly understood, what it always had been. By this time we were proficient enough to put together a full band, piano and bass included, and take on two or three engagements a week located within a maximum distance of fifty miles from the centre of London. We would meet up when our daily work was over, travel to a venue, perform for two or three hours, arrive back home early in the morning, sleep for a few hours, and then pick up again on our day jobs.

We were taken on by a small-time agent who was sure he could get work for us on an occasional, though fairly regular, basis. Some of these gigs were at established jazz clubs, but most of them were as makeshift as the agent himself, temporary spaces quickly adapted to earn money out of the Trad Boom. Anywhere would do: a dilapidated dockside warehouse, community centre, sports club, New Town shopping arcade, disused church hall, or a drinking club where the daytime regulars were driven out at seven o'clock, the place sprayed ineffectively with deodorant to be reopened as a jazz cellar an hour later. More enjoyably, and independently of the agent, we ran our own club in the back room of a pub in a comfortable Surrey suburb where we performed every Sunday evening.

It was a classic semi-pro situation. We hired the room, charged an entrance fee, set up a table at the door which was maintained by various friends, wives and girlfriends who travelled with us. They looked after the takings and saw that no one slipped in without paying. The landlord provided access to the pub bars, and, when business was good, would even open a small bar in a corner of the club room itself. For everyone concerned it was a cosy, enjoyable, and profitable, operation.

It was also far too cosy to last. Trad, we were to learn, hadn't been affiliated to Pop. It had been taken over. The welcoming cuddle was in truth a deadly embrace. The British pioneers were, in terms of money and popularity, doing very well indeed. They were now joined by large numbers of newly professional bands eager to create images that could be neatly branded, and by semi-pros like us who were satisfied with crumbs from the feast. The buzzword was presentation. Some bands settled for conventional smartness and dignity, others went for flamboyance. I don't personally remember seeing a jazz band dressed in deep-sea diving costumes or cowboy outfits replete from stetsons to spurs, but the most bizarre rumours flourished and awareness of the general trends that we ourselves were a tiny part of easily persuaded us that anything was possible.

Our agent would never have thought us worth the bother or expense of a fancy-dress costume, but when he arranged for us to appear at a north London ballroom, playing as interval support for one of the biggest of the big trad bands, he insisted that we do something about our customary everyday dress. This was too good a chance to miss, he lectured us, a platform, a showcase, the opportunity for hundreds of similar lucrative gigs to come. There was disagreement within the band about how we should respond to his advice. Eventually a compromise was reached that satisfied none of us. The plan was for us to kit ourselves out in black and blue striped blazers, slim jim ties, light grey flannels, and black shoes. We only escaped looking like seaside-promenading Edwardians by refusing to have anything to do with the straw boaters which the agent decided would provide just the right nifty finish to the outfit. Our rejection of the boaters he found incomprehensible, seeing it as nothing less than a denial of the Trad stardom that would, inevitably, have accompanied our acceptance of them. Not that his opinion mattered any longer. Or ours, come to that.

The interval performance went well enough for us to be invited to join the star band on stage for a couple of numbers, but even that moment of generous recognition was to carry only a personal significance. Our reluctant surrender to commercialism turned out to be as pointless as we feared it would be. It wasn't the fault of the boaters. Larger unseen forces were at work. Within a few weeks of our fleeting taste of stardom, the whole thing was over. The Trad Boom exploded. Overnight. Just like that! There weren't going to be dozens of repeat gigs in the future, or any come to that. Our uniforms were never used again.

The established bands, the British pioneers, our recent associates among them, survived, adjusting easily enough to the new conditions. Many of the lesser bands, recently professional or comfortably semi-pro, collapsed. Agents transferred their attention from amateurish trad bands to amateurish guitar-strumming teenagers. They were the ones now presented with contracts, club and concert gigs throughout Britain, spells in German or Dutch nightclubs where they could literally struggle to get their acts together, and promises of record promotions and television appearances. Anyone could have a go. Being or not being good enough still wasn't the main issue. For the moment at least. Time and the box office could be left to settle that issue.

One warm summer evening in the early Sixties we gathered as usual on a Sunday evening at our Surrey pub, organized the bandstand, set up a table at the entrance, and began to play. All was much as it had been for the previous couple of years, except that no one turned up to hear us. Not one paying customer walked through the door. The only people in the room were our various friends and relatives. We began our programme as normal, pretending that nothing had changed, though all the time waiting for some familiar faces to appear. Occasionally a potential customer would peer in at the door and retreat in embarrassment from the empty room. After a few of our regular numbers, we drifted into a tune which we had never played before. It was an old popular song, one of many which hadn't been born into jazz but which had long ago become part of the standard repertoire. Perhaps 'On the Sunny Side of the Street' or 'Skylark,' I'm no longer sure what tune it was, though I do remember starting it off by myself. I took it slowly, hesitantly, without consulting anyone else in the band, and making a shocking mess of it on the first run through, fluffing phrase after phrase, drifting along casually, experimenting rather than performing in the pathetically hollow room. I was gradually joined by the piano, rhythm section, and eventually the trombone and clarinet, each player concerned with getting the unaccustomed notes or chords right, caring little for any togetherness.

If the scene had been choreographed for a Hollywood musical, the seven of us would have stumbled about awkwardly for a while before blending into perfect harmony, culminating in a rousing final chorus. A crowd would have appeared as from nowhere, filling the dance floor, cheering its approval and crowning us with glory. But this wasn't Hollywood, there was no choreographer on hand, and musical triumph was the last thing on our minds. We played chorus after chorus, solo after solo, of the lovely old tune, slowly, inaccurately, funereally, providing a performance and atmosphere that matched to perfection our understanding that we were grinding to a halt, just like those old wind-up gramophones which had first fed my love of jazz. Except that this particular gramophone wasn't going to be rewound to keep the music going. It was a carefree gesture of defeat. We barely even spoke of it to each other, but simply packed our instruments, and went our separate ways.

What else was there for us to do as a band? We couldn't go back to the Centre or retreat to the hired rehearsal room that by this time had replaced it. Those days were gone. Nor was it really an option to change back from semi-pros to amateurs. At the start of the boom we had been astonished that anyone was willing to pay money at a door in order to enter a room to hear us play. But they had been, and in reasonably large numbers, though no longer. For some the sudden change in circumstances provoked a brief return to the old conflicts between the pure and the impure, now sharpened by bitter charges of betrayal. What did you do in the great Trad Boom, daddy? The established pioneers accepted a drop in their popularity, but survived by staying true to their now distinctive recognizable styles. The fly-by-nights in their outrageous costumes followed whatever alternative trends were on hand, while a fair number of gifted jazzmen who had been unexpectedly raised into professionalism but now had no audience, faced seriously hard times.

Semi-pros like us had to learn not only to do without the extra pocket money and the fun of performing in public but something more basic as well. What we had lost was a means of expression, good times, a way of life. Some dedicated semi-pros refused to accept the new circumstances and continued to play within the dramatically reduced market. They reformed their bands, often into smaller groups, and, if the publican was sympathetic transferred from a crowded back room to a corner in a local saloon bar where they were allowed to play for the faithful few on one of the pub's less busy nights. That's how I remember the scene the last time I saw it. Traditional jazz was already beginning to look like the refuge for the physically and musically middle aged that it would, in fact, remain for the next half-century. I decided I would prefer to stop playing the trumpet all together and take up other options instead.

I can't pretend that while these events were going on I gave much thought to Kenny Croft. Had he survived to experience the Trad Boom, I assumed that his response to it would have been fairly predictable. As in all things musical, he would have followed the example of his great mentor Ken Colyer and that path forward was classically straight and narrow. Colyer had denounced the commercialism that for a while seemed about to finish off revivalist jazz completely and refused to join the rush to the hit parade. He simply got on with the music, never pandering to his admirers but leaving them to seek him out, moving untiringly towards the moment when he would succeed in recreating the ideal New Orleans sound that he himself had experienced as a young man. That, surely, was the model Kenny would have adopted. As we had never granted him an identity separate from Colyer's, so we could hardly have thought him capable of striking out on his own. In the days of plenty there had been money enough to support a number of other Colyer-inspired bands so why shouldn't Kenny's have joined them? Who could possibly have been better qualified for such a role?

Nowadays I find myself less happy with that old certainty. It would be ungenerous to dispense with it entirely, but no longer does it deserve unqualified support. In destroying promise so decisively, an early death places a very shaky question mark over the direction unfulfilled development might have taken. It becomes impossible to assess what changes of mind and purpose there could have been. Nothing is truly certain. For Kenny, artistic potential was not an issue. There was nothing experimental about his playing, no thought of musical development of any kind except backwards, as it were, to New Orleans. Any conjecture along these lines has to be personal, and based on any time-frozen images of him my memory can summon up.

There are several of these for me to choose among. There he is, possibly only a figment of my imagination, in refurbished school uniform with a New Orleans bandsman's cap perched incongruously on his head. Or, not imagined at all but very much the real thing, bumping into him at Charing Cross railway station on a Saturday evening. He on his way to Colyer's and me to Cy's, neither of us attaching any importance to the meeting, both of us thinking only of our own different musical experiences to come. These are images of a steadfastness that was never to be tested and they can be left securely in their frozen condition. They are not, however, the picture of Kenny that stays most forcefully with me.

That is a photograph of a group rather than an individual. The Kenny Croft New Orleans Jazzmen lined up ready to start rehearsals on Sunday mornings at the Centre. As always, the musicians are smartly dressed in their simple uniforms of dark grey flannels, white shirts, and black ties. They also have with them their musical and publicity accoutrements – the billboard with the band's name painted upon it, the metal bowler hats clipped to adjustable stands, the whole picture framed by the otherwise empty spaces of the large doorless room. Are they gazing back to New Orleans, reviving the past, enacting their dreams? Yes, of course, they were doing that, as we all were. But isn't it possible that they could have been gazing forward as well, looking ahead, enacting dreams of a very different, more private, less easily confessed kind?

Move three or four years on and they would have been the very type of new successful Trad band. For as long as we knew them they had nurtured exactly the kind of collective image that flourished during the Boom. Every rehearsal a performance, always playing as though to a full rather than an empty room; learning to clap in harmony with Kenny's singing; encouraging their as yet non-existent audience to join in; acting out the full part. Compared with our studied amateurism and bohemian dress, they were already polished professionals. Were they aware of what all of this might come to? If so, it didn't deflect them from their New Orleans ideal, at least not then at that stage of their development. But add on a couple of years, give them an agent on the make, a full diary, a catchy arrangement of a popular tune that is an unexpected hit with non-jazz fans, and who knows where, or how, they might have ended up.

The fact that they were purists and Colyer devotees wouldn't necessarily have held them back. Some of the biggest of the Trad stars had emerged from the same stable, including the bandleader we had performed with in that north London ballroom. Is it possible that Kenny might have become a renegade? And if so, would he have suffered terrible guilt at having betrayed the cause? Or would he have shrugged his bony shoulders and accepted his good fortune? It's a uneasy line of thought. Goodness, we might have ended up as an interval filler for the Kenny Croft New Orleans Jazzmen!

But nothing like that was going to happen. Kenny had been arbitrarily wiped out of such considerations, while I, left just as arbitrarily alive and free to choose, stopped playing the trumpet, and began thinking of a life with books in ways I had never considered before. There was no regret on my part, no feeling of resentment that things had been forced upon me by the implosion of the Trad Boom. It did not even clash discordantly with the attitudes and values that had guided me for most of my young life. Traditional jazz may owe a great deal to the blues, a philosophy grounded in loss and deprivation, but it has also always joyfully embraced the present and welcomed the inevitability of moving on. And in Britain (as so often in America) the jazz scene had changed direction. It was time for me to recognize that a very specific historical moment had passed and to move on.

* * * *

For some years I gave up listening to jazz as well as trying to play it. This again had nothing to do with disillusionment or even or loss of interest. Nor were there any rival musical attractions involved. There was no possibility that I would follow the example of so many of the casual trad musicians of the Fifties and Sixties and switch to the now ubiquitous pop music or, more particularly, to rock or the newly emerging electronic music. There was nothing to tempt me in any of that. Nor was I drawn to stay generally with jazz and go mainstream or modern. In so far as I continued to pay any attention to jazz at all, I stayed in Chicago (or thereabouts), and gradually developed an enthusiastic interest in classical music, especially piano and chamber music, all of which had been previously unknown to me. It turned out to be a wonderfully complementary interest as well. Between Chicago jazz and European chamber music, I found no resentment, no jostling for attention, no unwillingness to share space or time, no violent reaction one upon the other. They were fully accepting and tolerant of each other, happy to coexist. A Louis Armstrong Hot Five and a Beethoven string quartet; a Jelly Roll Morton piano solo and a Chopin nocturne; 'Mabel's Dream' and 'Death and the Maiden.' Because I was never driven to reject my youthful absorption in traditional jazz I was able to carry it forward with me, allowing it to rest effortlessly with new, seemingly very different sounds.

At the Centre we had known instinctively, and at a time when few Americans shared our feelings, that what we were struggling to play in so amateur and imitative a manner was classic American music. Nowadays, those early crude instincts of ours have been translated into the generally unobjectionable claim, made by no one more enthusiastically than Americans, that jazz *is* America's great, distinctive contribution to classical music. Instinct first, reason later. That's how it has to be, and, for us that was how it always had been.

And it remained so for me until sometime in the late 1980s when reason (or age, perhaps) intervened, telling me to look back and at least try to understand how life had been at a time when reason was not even consulted and instinct had flourished, joyfully uncontrolled. What I undertook was partly an historical exercise, partly a personal one. I decided I would try listening to (for the very first time in some cases) the kind of jazz I had once happily dismissed without thought. I began, conventionally enough, with Dizzy Gillespie and Charlie Parker and then moved on. I even bought a box set of Fats Navarro CDs! That was me coming to terms with what I still thought of as modern jazz. Although I wasn't completely taken over by it, as I once had been by

Bunk Johnson and Freddie Keppard, I was no longer eager to dismiss it untried. Essential connections that had of course been there all the time were soon making themselves felt, and some of what I heard I greatly enjoyed.

Welcome as this was, it was merely a first step and not the main or ultimate purpose of my quest. What I wanted to do was to try to reassess the revivalist jazz that had absorbed so much of my early life. For many years I had shut out even the desire to think of jazz in terms of any kind of change or development. I had stayed content with what I had, not wanting it challenged or changed in any way at all. Now, in effect for the first time, I felt a strong need to know what, if anything, had happened after we had performed our spontaneous funeral dirge all those years ago on a warm Sunday evening in the empty back room of our cosy Surrey pub. The answer I received was astonishing, unlike anything I had expected.

It emerged that jazz in Britain hadn't been at death's door on that gloomy Sunday in Surrey. Not only had it survived or perhaps experienced a miraculous rebirth, it was actually flourishing. From the radio I learned there was live jazz all around me, as near or distant as I wanted it to be. I didn't know anyone connected with it, but there it was all right, greatly admired, if hardly popular. It was quite obviously still a minority interest, attracting a small amount of favourable media attention if little general acclaim. In some respects the overall situation didn't feel that much different from the 1950s. There was even present a good helping of the old evangelical spirit. But the jazz itself was totally different. Much of what I heard I didn't even think of *as* jazz.

The old absolute divisions between types of jazz were largely irrelevant to this new young generation of jazz musicians, along with any sense of revivalism. To them, Chicago was as antiquated as New Orleans, while Gillespie, Parker and the rest of the musicians I was continuing to regard as modern masters were now as far in the past as New Orleans had once been to us. Nor were these young jazz musicians interested in separating out these modern figures from everyone else and treating them with the blind hero worship we had so willingly offered up to Bunk Johnson,

George Lewis and Louis Armstrong. They were also just as likely to be black as white, unashamedly collaborating with rock and electronic music, while in their everyday attitudes and voices remaining as British as we had ever been. They could even be heard claiming an outrageously daring 'Britishness' for their jazz, striving to give to it an independence from its American roots that would have been incomprehensible to us.

And, although we would have been incapable of understanding it at the time, I began to see that it was the fading away of all those passionate schisms and fine distinctions, the passing of a very particular moment in traditional jazz, that we had been mourning. If we had ever bothered to take any notice of the Mods, our implacable opponents of the 1950s, we might have been aware that even then they had no thought of disappearing. They had never shared in, or competed for, the fleeting popular glory enjoyed by their traditional rivals. They would have observed its demise without regret, and continued to play and grow and develop in their own peculiar ways. They were the ones who had gone underground and carried on fighting, and their success had encouraged the emergence of this new combative breed of British jazz musicians. Some of the Trad pioneers were still around, augmented by disciples from my own generation, all of them elderly now but continuing to play and attract audiences, middle-aged ones I reasonably supposed.

Cy Laurie and Ken Colyer were sadly no longer alive, though their recordings were available and still sounding fresh enough to bring vividly back to mind the passionate conflicts their contrasting styles once aroused. I was especially fascinated to see that Colyer's reputation especially looked not only more secure than ever, but had somehow managed to retain exactly the same kind of admiration it always had. His name and recordings were still treasured and kept alive by devoted followers, his legendary status and future assured, the sound he created very much his own.

Personally impressed as I was by the nature of Colyer's survival and capable now of enjoying his music in a new way, it also meant that I was happy to credit Kenny Croft with a degree of sensitivity I had never granted him before. These, though, were personal responses and it mattered still more to me that Colyer had survived at all, along with Cy Laurie, Chris Barber, Humphrey Lyttleton, and the rest. All of them were there, segments of a glorious kaleidoscope of twentieth-century jazz, set to take their chances on whatever futures they might have, ready to be judged by the quality of the recorded evidence they had left behind them. All of it, from revivalist to avant-garde, continues to be bound indissolubly to America – there can really be no such thing as a jazz that isn't fundamentally American – but asserting the right of their various sounds and identities to a place in a history of jazz that is now no longer simply American. All those ancient ideological battles weren't pointless or unfruitful. They were assertions of personal involvement, determined attempts to assert the value of, and to stake a claim in, a great and thrilling new art form. As long, of course, as ours was accepted as the right claim, and we were quite sure it was.

All too sure, no doubt, but necessarily and inevitably so. Some future musical court will have no trouble finding us guilty of imitating the imitators, of copying the copyists, but I now know that when that happens it will be possible to call the gramophone dramatically and decisively to our aid. That should at least exonerate us from the more damaging charges. The evidence is clear enough. We were guilty of a totally harmless passion for what was often derided at the time but can now be claimed quite reasonably as the most original music of the twentieth century. There can't be anything pernicious about this. As any record shop, online or in the local high street, will testify, the contribution made to the movement by the British revivalists hasn't been swept away entirely. It still might have to go, but not just now, not yet.

And the reason is clear. It was revivalism itself that triumphed. That's what happened. It became British revivalism, European revivalism. Linked irrevocably to America, but at the same time unmistakably *not* American, the best of the British revivalists are distinctively themselves. The victory was not down to any one inspiring individual or band, or the collected efforts of the very best of those musicians: it was the total effect that mattered. Driven by love, scorning even to think in terms of any kind of racism, inspired by the spirit of jazz, revivalism continued the movement that began originally with the exodus from New Orleans, spreading the message to Chicago, New York, Kansas and every other American city, and then on to London, Manchester, Edinburgh, Paris, Stockholm and beyond. Jazz was not simply transported to those places, and to so many others within Britain and throughout the world. On the way it transformed itself effortlessly from black to white, just as it had done in America where the continuous experimentalism in jazz has long been pursued, with individual triumphs achieved by both white and black musicians.

It was transplanted as well as transported, protected, nurtured, and permitted to develop a character of its own, the geniuses of the different places collaborating fruitfully with the founding genius of New Orleans. That is what the current jazz scene, featuring music that I find it difficult even to accept as jazz, is still about. And if this is a matter of offshoots that can never be truly independent of their roots, well, there's nothing much wrong with that. Quite the opposite, really. It's those shared roots that have encouraged a constant flow of individual worldwide contributions to jazz. And it's those same shared roots that might eventually allow British revivalism to shed its present reputation as a quaint and local scholarly preoccupation and be allotted a place of its own in jazz history. A small one, of course, but distinctive enough, and honourable.

Monica

Criticism is a study by which men grow important and formidable at very small expense. The power of invention has been conferred by nature upon few, and the labour of learning those sciences which may, by mere labour, be obtained, is too great to be willingly endured; but every man can exert such judgement as he has upon the works of others.

Dr Johnson, *The Idler*. No. 60, 9 June 1759

I first met Monica at the University of Leicester a few days before the start of the 1968-9 academic year. The occasion was a staff meeting of the English department, and I can date it with some precision because in those days, for reasons I have never properly understood, the academic year always began around the tenth or eleventh of October. Perhaps it still does. It's now a long time since the daily routine of university life mattered to me one way or another, but that used to be the custom. British universities were then, and no doubt still are, canonical in all matters relating to their calendars, so the date of my first meeting with Monica is easy to fix. It would have been the eighth or ninth of October 1968, give or take a day or two either way.

Staff meetings of this kind were held by most departments at fairly regular points during term-time, perhaps every month, sometimes as often as once a week. Occasionally they needed to be placed just inside or outside vacations. As they are usually given over to mundane routine and regarded by many of those obliged to attend as a necessary waste of time, they rank among the most forgettable moments of academic life. But for me at least, there were good personal reasons why this particular meeting has stayed in my mind.

I was the new boy in the department, an assistant lecturer on probation, just about to begin my career as a university teacher, and attending for the very first time a gathering of my new colleagues. I had not yet delivered a lecture or taken a tutorial, or met any of the students I would be teaching. All of this made me as inexperienced in the ways of university teaching as anyone who is actually part of the system is ever likely to be.

The English department met to settle its internal affairs in the study or 'room,' as, in those early days of levelling down such places were coming to be called, of Professor A. R. ('Arthur') Humphreys who had been in charge of things for as long as any but the very oldest of his colleagues could remember. His study was in a restored eighteenth-century building that over the years had served as a country house, a hospital – or more properly a lunatic asylum some said, accompanying their words with a knowing smile – and a recuperation centre for wounded servicemen. It was now given over to higher education.

In the university's early days, the 1920s, this handsome building would have contained within its ivy-covered walls pretty well the whole educational experience: teachers, students, administrators, and librarians as well. Now it provided the campus with a dignified focal point while functioning primarily as the university's administrative centre. The handful of senior members of staff who still lodged in it were there on sufferance. Their tenancy seemed permanent enough but it was, and always had been, temporary. Necessarily so, because the entire campus was in a continuous process of trying to establish a collective identity for itself. Over the years, it had become a jumble of buildings of different ages and various types, many of which were accepted as transient. Everyone survived on the promised certainty of a bright, so far undated, educational future. Meanwhile, the haphazard past was everywhere on view, and a convincing present barely visible at all.

The personal rooms of most members of the teaching staff were dotted about the campus regardless of departments and disciplines. My own room was in a long prefabricated shed which had been built originally to house nurses during the First World War and was still awaiting demolition. The walls were so thin that a tutorial discussion in one of the rooms couldn't risk getting too lively in case it interrupted a tutorial on a quite different subject taking place in an adjoining room, while consultations of a private matter with students or staff had to be whispered to prevent any confidences from being overheard by anyone standing in the corridor outside. The building looked exactly like the single-storey structures that generations of children have built with playing cards, the enjoyment coming from skilfully balancing a large number of cards in line against each other and then laying them low with a casual flick of a finger.

And sure enough, after I had been at Leicester for about a year that image was activated. It was time for the ancient nursing block to go. Its inhabitants were all evacuated, leaving the long flimsy structure looking desolate. A bulldozer was brought up to the front door and began its operation with a tentative bull-like prod. The whole building collapsed instantly and neatly into a pile of thin wooden playing-card walls. For some fifty years it had remained intact and served its different functions with virtually no foundations at all.

The teachers now occupied rooms in a slim, multi-storied, purpose-built tower block with impressively deep foundations. During construction these had been surrounded by high protective wooden fences dotted with peepholes that allowed everyone to watch the foundations being dug and to savour the evidence that this time permanence was on offer. The amount of space each department was allotted in the tower depended on its size and academic importance. If large, it could claim one or two floors all to itself: if small, it was allotted only a half or third share. For some of the departments it was the first time their scattered members had ever been housed together. Whatever their status and however high they had to rise in the tower to reach their new homes, all were carried skyward, half a dozen at a time, in a futuristic, perilously open, ever-moving paternoster lift.

The tower foretold a definite end to Leicester's higgledy-piggledy architectural image. There would be no more putting up with totally unsuitable buildings year after year just because they were readily available. Nor were there to be any more staff meetings in Arthur Humphreys' elegant study. No longer any elegant study for Arthur come to that. Like everyone else, he was now to begin his mornings with a nervous shuffle onto the paternoster, the necessary prelude for transportation to his allotted space, its extent decided according to academic status by government decree. Only the administrators, left triumphantly in charge of the country house, remained at ground level.

The whole exercise had been undertaken primarily to ease pressure on Leicester's overcrowded campus, and this it achieved. It would also, though such matters seem to have been little considered in Britain's belated dash to expand higher education in the late 1960s, spell an end to the intimate atmosphere of teaching and scholarship that had long been an ideal embraced by all universities in England regardless of their wealth, educational status, or architectural grandeur. The model followed was the Oxbridge collegiate system of small-group tutorial teaching, and could be regarded as a feasible ambition for everyone because at that time only a tiny proportion of the population attended any kind of university. For something like ninety-five percent of young people, it meant nothing at all. Large civic universities clothed their devotion to the Oxbridge ideal in an outward display of Victorian urban grandeur, while small regional or provincial university colleges like Leicester centred themselves semi-rurally on dignified country houses and lived much of the time in makeshift housing. Nor was there immediately any major change in the early 1960s with the founding of five 'new' English universities.

The earliest of these carried public images that in terms of mood and setting were anything but new. Nor were they, in truth, any less Oxbridge-inspired than their immediate predecessors. Like many of the regional universities they were built on former country estates, but there the comparison pretty well ended. The new universities were designed with plenty of room around them for coordinated development, whereas places like Leicester had been left to grow randomly, adding a bit here and there whenever necessary. The new universities couldn't even claim, with any fairness, that they were democratizing higher education. It's true that student numbers increased, but not in any spectacular way. What was taking place was a one-off experiment rather than a purposeful step forward. There was some talk in the media about the classlessness of the new universities, and a good deal more about their glamorous, trend-setting contributions to Sixties' Britain.

But the most influential feature of the new universities was probably the systematic planning that had gone into founding them. This went largely unremarked by the media, but its significance was not lost on regional universities. Shocked and irritated by their upstart rivals, jealous and contemptuous in equal measure, they knew they couldn't compete with the party atmosphere even if they had wanted to. Systematic planning, though, was a different matter. Suddenly here was something everyone wanted, and there was nothing fashionable or trendy about how to get it. The case was a straightforward one of years of neglect and being constantly passed over. It was quickly made and accepted. Within a decade of the foundation stones being laid at the newest of the new universities, the prefabricated nursing shed in Leicester where I had conducted my first tutorials was being flattened. That was the past cleared away. The present was the open, ever-moving platforms of the paternoster. Step on quickly or wait for the next compartment to arrive. Where it was taking us all when we did manage to clamber aboard was far from certain. As I remember it, no one talked of the future. We were too busy confronting the present and the changes that were beginning to tumble, in a very unplanned manner, upon us.

It was farewell not only to a moment in time when academics occupied studies rather than rooms, but also one in which a Professor of English might still think of himself as capable of buying and reading all the major books on his subject. Not simply all those items relevant to his special interests, but pretty well everything on the subject he had been appointed to profess. Apart from a relatively small number of technical and specialist monographs, many of these were also books which it was assumed educated people outside of Academia might want to read or at least know about.

There they had all been, lining the walls of Arthur Humphreys' spacious country-house study with its unnaturally high ceiling and ornate cornices. The books were carefully organized according to literary period, Anglo-Saxon to the present day, texts together with commentaries, standing neatly on wooden shelves that reached from floor to ceiling. Along the tops of the shelved books there were others packed horizontally with still more heaped on the carpeted floor in front of the bookcases. That the books were so obviously overflowing their shelves at an alarming rate was a clear enough indication that the subject was in the process of outgrowing itself just as rapidly as the institution that had spawned it.

When staff meetings were to be held, a curious assortment of chairs, ranging in type from desk and dining through to what looked suspiciously like bar stools, would suddenly appear scattered about the room. They were brought in to supplement the several armchairs that were always there. As members of the department arrived they chose whichever chair they fancied. There was no departmental status involved in these choices, no order of seniority detailing where everyone should sit, a system I had heard was still firmly in operation at certain other universities. Anything of that sort would have been entirely alien to Leicester's liberal spirit. Inevitably a certain amount of posturing took place as people moved into position. That will always be the case whenever chairs and a group of people are gathered together. But, regardless of how such matters may have been handled elsewhere, at Leicester we were democratic in our choosing of the chairs.

It seemed, therefore, entirely fitting that departmental business should be conducted in Arthur's study under his broad-minded auspices, with all the rest of us crammed tightly together, sitting in or on our personally selected chairs, any local rivalries temporarily subdued by the communal nature of the event, the entire gathering steeped in an atmosphere of benign judiciousness. Unsurprisingly, I arrived far too early for my first staff meeting. Seated conspicuously alone as my new colleagues trickled in and occupied the chairs around me, I was, just as unsurprisingly, good-heartedly ribbed for being overeager.

Monica was the last to arrive, forcing the door open with some difficulty because she was dragging behind her a bulky travelling bag. There were no chairs left and I thought it a pity she was obliged to occupy a bar stool. Later I realized it had probably been left free for her, that it was almost impossible to think of her as sunk down in an armchair or, indeed, seated trim and upright on any sort of chair. She was a natural percher, the departmental parrot or cockatoo, a nodder and pecker, more brightly coloured than the rest of us, and noisier when she wanted to be. My first impression of her, though, was not ornithological: it was drawn from the early autumn atmosphere that was already beginning to settle around the university.

She was made up like a rather classy November the Fifth guy, her lips stickily red, her eyes hugely transformed by thick pendant splodges of black mascara and flamboyant winged spectacles. She had reddish-blond hair which jutted out from her head at odd angles, and she was short, not above five foot three or four, I would guess, and putting on weight. Some women worry about these things as they move into middle age, some go along with them. Monica was obviously a goer-along-with-them. She was wearing a fine silk blouse the colour of tea roses, the delicacy of which was obliterated by a hip-huggingly tight pillar-box red miniskirt which she hoisted high up her thighs before clambering on the stool. When she was comfortably ensconced she crossed her podgy legs which were covered by black fishnet tights and jammed into red high-heeled shoes. Easing her skirt even further up so that it was now bunched around her hips and almost ceasing technically to be a skirt at all, she announced, 'OK. That's me!'

With what sounded very much like Monica's permission for him to start, Arthur opened the proceedings. He referred back to some business left over from the previous academic year and brought the new session into play, warmly welcoming me to the department with a few characteristically well-turned comments. Then he bounced one finger round the room like a child playing dib-dab-dob and gave me an introductory name for everyone present, saying something like, 'I don't think you've yet met....' Or 'Have you met.....?' When he got to Monica he named her three times as though he himself was unclear who exactly this member of his department was: 'Miss Jones...Monica...Monica Jones.'

As always alert to musical references, I imagined him transforming his introduction into a slick chorus of the Rodgers and Hart song 'Have you met Miss Jones?' but there was nothing jaunty about Arthur's awkwardness. It hung around for a moment and then disappeared. Later I would understand that this kind of ambiguity often accompanied Monica and at that time, of course, other women of a similar status and position. A doctorate would have settled the matter, but they were far less common in her generation than mine, and anyway, as I would soon learn, it was impossible to imagine Monica wanting such a thing let alone going for it. There were also then, with or without doctorates, far fewer women teaching in universities and the slightly uncertain academic parlance of the time reflected the fact. She was Miss Jones officially to her students and university staff; Monica to her colleagues; and, when a still friendly though semi-formal identity was required, Monica Jones. There was no sign of her having noticed anything unusual in Arthur's manner. She nodded her head and flashed a vigorous smile at me, exposing as she did so a set of spectacularly uneven, decaying, brown and yellow teeth jutting out of lurid pink gums.

As soon as the meeting was officially closed Monica moved to the door, tugging her travelling bag along the floor, pausing in the now crowded centre of the room to chat with colleagues, reasserting friendships, catching up on news after the long vacation. Even so, she was clearly eager to get away. I didn't get to speak to her then, though I had learned from her occasional contributions to the meeting that her voice was as singular as every other aspect of her. Rich and full, though projected through a good deal of spluttering and, as much of what she said had aimed for a comic effect, a lot of throaty giggles as well.

I had been asked by Arthur to stay behind for a few minutes, and once we were alone he gave me some advice on how to proceed in my new job. I already had a list of the names of the students I would be teaching. These had been organized into tutorial groups and Arthur added some necessary details, suggesting which of the set authors I might like to start with and, once I had settled arrangements in my own mind, how I was to contact my students. Although the advice could hardly have been more basic, it was, apart from being asked to sit in on a couple of tutorials given by a senior member of the department and Arthur himself monitoring one of my lectures, the only formal guidance I was ever to receive on how to teach at university level.

Not that that surprised me. In fact, it had never occurred to me to that I might have needed any advice on how to run a tutorial to deliver a lecture to a hundred or so students. If anyone had suggested I did I would probably have resented it. After all, behind me were six dedicated student years: three as an undergraduate, and then, immediately, a further three as a postgraduate. It was true that in that time I had done only a very small amount of teaching, but so what? Teaching was, surely, a natural extension of my research and writing, both of which would continue much as before. As an undergraduate I had been actively and enthusiastically supported by my tutors. Later I was guided in my research by an excellent supervisor. Much of the time was like serving an apprenticeship rather than acting out the traditional carefree image of a student. From the start, this world of learning and writing had been somewhere in which I felt instantly at home. I had been encouraged to develop that feeling and follow it through. Universities, it has often been said, are self-perpetuating institutions. And so they are, or at least were very strongly so then, and I was a beneficiary.

With such a background, how could I possibly have known that succession wasn't a clear or easy thing, that a change in my status from research student to member of staff had little to do with continuity or even continuation, that these were qualities not on generous offer but to be fought for? If I felt occasionally as though I was being launched on a solitary journey of uncertain destination, that was understandable enough, nothing more than a bit of local nervousness. A life of enviable independence was one the main attractions held out by the career I was entering, and that belief had now been reinforced by the introduction of the second crucial element of the academic equation. Hadn't I just, that very morning, been welcomed into a community of scholars, men and women who shared with me and their students much the same values, standards and attitudes, and on whose support I would in future be able to draw with confidence?

Here it all was, the classic 'idea of a university.' Individual freedom within a supportive community dedicated to shared educational and cultural ideas, a body of like-minded men and women ready and eager to welcome me in.

* * * *

When I was formally appointed to an assistant lectureship at Leicester in the summer of 1968 the responses of people generally in the know about such matters were surprisingly uniform. 'A nice place, very friendly,' they said. It was the English department they had in mind. 'Very nice indeed. The friendliest anywhere.' Their tone was different if the university or the city of Leicester was being referred to. Then the friendliness was absorbed within its Midlands setting and I was seen as heading for somewhere 'a bit dull,' or 'flat,' 'not too exciting.' If a literary quote was called for, Hilaire Belloc's view of the English Midlands as 'sodden and unkind' was ready to hand.

The English department itself, though, escaped even these topographical strictures. Everyone agreed it was very pleasant. Perhaps a trifle smug, but nevertheless unrivalled for its niceness. That's what they all said. The implication, often present in such comments though never expressed openly and not something I would have understood at the time, was that in this respect Leicester truly was unusual, not at all what one would normally expect.

And these unvoiced assumptions were right. Compared with other English departments I would experience later, Leicester was exceptionally, perhaps uniquely, warm and welcoming. This was due almost entirely to it having been shaped and patterned for so many years by Arthur Humphreys. His formative influence became apparent within moments of meeting him, though it was a puzzle for me, and no doubt for others, to grasp how that influence could have been exerted for so long. It wasn't simply that he didn't look of a suitable age to be someone with such a reputation for wise authority. He didn't look any particular age at all. I could never work out whether he was surprisingly young or prematurely aged. It was as though he was still outgrowing his potential in the way that some children are said to be outgrowing their strength. In their case, the conventional wisdom is that they will eventually reach a natural stopping point: meanwhile, there is nothing to worry about. But Arthur seemed to have become trapped arbitrarily somewhere he didn't want to be. The career pattern I imagined for him was that of a young man who had raced ahead, quickly obtained the chair of English at provincial Leicester and then, realizing he wasn't sure where exactly he was supposed to go next, settled down to a dignified middle age. It would have been then, I imagined, while he was waiting for everyone else to catch up, that he had read and accumulated the books that lined his university study. All of this would have to have taken place in the late 1940s and the 1950s. Or at least that was how it seemed to me in the late 1960s.

Together with Arthur's indeterminate age, and just as clearly on open display, were the personal qualities that left no doubt why he was so admired for his leadership skills. He was a model of calm, order, and respectability; punctiliously liberal and judicious; handsome in an ageless, well-cut manner; always charming and relaxed, though at the same time rather distant and slightly faded. He was also devotedly married. His wife, always on hand, invariably present on public and departmental occasions, smartly dressed, diplomatic, a royal consort, was herself the epitome of what in those far-off days an academic wife was ideally expected to be.

If there was a flaw in the shimmering perfection of Arthur's public image, it was his academic standing which was undistinguished. For some years his scholarly reputation had rested on a rather old-fashioned literature and society study of Augustan England, though by the time I went to Leicester he was becoming better known for several prestigious editions of Shakespeare's history plays. It was characteristic of his unstainable personality that his meagre scholarly record was interpreted, with uncharacteristic academic generosity and in terms entirely favourable to him. The reason why he had not yet made a more impressive scholarly showing was generally explained away in terms of his devotion to the department, any early ambitions he may have had having been sacrificed to the relentless demands of administration. He himself would never have thought of making this a complaint, though he did allow it to be known that he was looking forward to getting back once again to real work. It was the first of very many times I was to hear this excuse in universities. In Arthur's case it may have been true, but I doubt it. For beneath his committed sense to true proportion in all things, there was a strain of sadness that he was never able totally to conceal.

Maybe the cause was deep inside him and therefore unknowable, it being impossible to imagine him ever confiding his innermost feelings to anyone, except perhaps his wife. It may have been that because he had devoted all of his energy to the creation of a friendly English department he had failed to write the books that would have brought him a name and with it the opportunity to move on to a more prestigious university position. But who could know? Maybe he simply didn't have what it takes to write such books. Whatever the reason, and like it or not, he was obviously there at Leicester for ever and ever. If that was his personal dilemma – and, after all, there are worse academic fates – then appearing to be so at ease in the role wasn't helping him to get out of it. It was as though he could never totally conceal a yearning to be a different kind of person from the one he indisputably was. And if that isn't burden enough for someone to carry around all the time, there would have been the additional realization that he was pretty well incapable of changing anything, let alone his own nature.

He was bound top to toe by the good opinion that was universally held of him. He was the type of professor, truly, in my experience, rare beyond price, who was admired not for his scholarly achievements, ideological soundness, or good writing, any one of which qualities he might well have been thrilled to flaunt, but simply for being himself. He was a famously kind and generous man. Not exactly self-effacing, but undeniably just and good. That, though, was not enough. It rarely is. There had to be something wrong, some flaw or weakness; something, for others if not for himself, that would lessen the goodness, or at least explain it away. And so there was, or rather, so his friends and colleagues liked to believe.

Way back, when Arthur applied for the Leicester chair, there had been some kind of protest against him, a demonstration in which both staff and students were involved. The protesters wanted the job to be given not to the young outsider but to another candidate, a respected scholar and much-liked teacher who was already a member of the department. The Appointments Board turned down the insider in favour of Arthur. For a while the atmosphere was rumoured to have been very disagreeable, as one can imagine it would have been, but Arthur hung on. His rival for the chair behaved with notable decency, accepted the decision that had gone against him, and soon the troubles were resolved. Not forgotten, though. Nothing of this kind ever is. Not in universities.

These events were some twenty years in the past when I arrived in Leicester. By then the Arthur Humphreys affair was old news. Totally irrelevant as well. Leicester was at last on the move, caught up in the expansion that had been denied it for so long. It was a time to look forward rather than back. During his stewardship Arthur had brought some seventeen or eighteen new members of staff into the department and expansion was by no means at an end. My own appointment itself had about it something of a symbolic role. I was an incomer from the very first of those new universities which had aroused such ambivalent feelings in the academic establishment. All of my colleagues had come from more traditional academic backgrounds, and hardly any of them could have been at Leicester at the time of Arthur's disruptive appointment.

Even so, I had the incident narrated to me by several of my new colleagues the moment I arrived as though it was the kind of information I really couldn't do without. It was there on a level with how to find my way to the library or how I could register for the unbelievably generous free stationery allowance given at that time by the university to all members of staff. How was it possible for me to begin to come to terms with my new job without knowing at once that my boss, the man in charge of the friendliest department of English in the country, had not always been so respected or even wanted by his colleagues? Nor was it the only piece of information about him that was regarded as essential.

I was also constantly recommended to read Malcolm Bradbury's novel *Eating People is Wrong* which had been first published a decade earlier in 1959. 'Bradbury was a student here,' I was assured as though that gave him unassailable credibility, 'and Professor Treece is Arthur. There's no doubt about it. Especially the moment when...'

It was characteristic of how closely Arthur was identified with the department that when he did finally decide to hand over the running of it to someone else, the news should have been treated as momentous. A formal announcement simply wasn't enough. It needed to be reinforced by constant repetition, passed on from one person to another as though only repetition could stave off total disbelief. Arthur himself was frequently congratulated at having attained a greatly deserved liberty, and he responded with visible delight. So fulsome was the attention to an event that anywhere else would have been treated as matter of fact, that I had to remind myself of the true scale of what was happening. Arthur hadn't been diagnosed as suffering from a terminal illness. Nor was he leaving Leicester to take up an Oxbridge chair or being awarded a knighthood for services to education. He would still be with us, actively on hand, but simply no longer in charge. Someone else had taken over his departmental responsibilities.

That someone was the holder of the second chair of English, Professor Philip Collins, a noted Dickens specialist and chairman of the recently established Victorian Studies Centre. I had been, in effect, Philip's choice for the new lectureship, appointed primarily to help teach within his areas of academic interest. These were currently fashionable and still on their way up, whereas Arthur's specialisms (eighteenth-century literature and Shakespeare) were already suffering from a lack of popularity and having to be force-fed to students.

After so many years of Arthur, the appointment of a new head of department was a novelty to virtually everyone. But although regarded with some apprehension the transition was entirely painless. Fears, expressed with shivers of anticipation, that we would all be adrift without Arthur to guide us and that Philip wouldn't be capable of matching the achievements of his predecessor, were groundless. So were predictions of inevitable future conflicts between the old and the new. Wasn't it just possible that there could even be something of a rerun of the trauma surrounding Arthur's initial appointment, with Arthur now playing the part of a resentful incumbent and Philip the unwanted upstart pretender? No it wasn't possible at all, and nothing of the sort happened. In staff meetings, now held in a shiny, anonymous, bookless seminar room in the tower, Arthur was clearly more than happy to join the ranks and sit on a plastic chair while Philip directed the proceedings from the top of the table. There was no power struggle, no bitterness, no collapse of leadership.

What we did experience, though, was a distinct change of mood and tempo brought about by the contrasting personalities of the two men. The atmosphere of friendliness continued, but it was now forceful, assertive, boisterous rather than subdued. Nor was it able to function any longer as a general model for others to observe with admiration. It was its own combative self, the niceness thinned out to reveal some previously concealed sharp edges.

Successful academics often take on, or at least act out in public, the distinguishing qualities of their special interests. In such cases it is not easy to distinguish between cause and effect. It may be that many of them are genuinely attracted to the social, moral or personal qualities they discover in their chosen subject or author. Or perhaps they simply don't have sufficient individuality to do otherwise, much as great actors are often said not to have a personality of their own because they are always on the way to becoming someone else. There was certainly a strong element of this at Leicester.

With Arthur in charge, the department was marked by the assumed Augustan virtues of decorum, order, balance, reason, and control, the qualities which Arthur himself always took pains to represent. In contrast, Philip's reign was typified by a burgeoning sense of drive and energy, as though driven by a mission to inject a good dose of bustling Victorianism and big-hearted Dickensianism into our quiet little corner of Augustan Leicester.

He was a highly emotional, truly kind-hearted man, passionately eager to be involved, always keen to do things and to be seen to be doing them, especially when it was a matter of colleagues or students facing some kind of crisis in their lives. Everything about him was what in the years to come would be described as upfront. Whereas it was possible to spend some time in Arthur's company without being made aware of any particular literary interests he might have had, Philip declared his specialism immediately you met him. His academic reputation had been made with several books on Dickens. They were historical in approach, controversially and courageously opposed to the poorly defined, impressionistic critical dogma known as practical criticism that was then still rampant in English departments. He talked endlessly of Dickens, and would ruthlessly change back to the right path any conversation that he felt was drifting too far in the direction of another author. He liked to draw attention to supposed similarities between himself and his literary hero, and some of these could certainly be made to appear startling.

When I first got to know him he had recently married a former student who was some years younger than himself. It was Philip's second marriage. The first had been childless and he was keen to have children, lots of them if possible. That wish was quickly granted and Philip set about transforming the Collins household into a model of Victorian domesticity. He was a good host, and greatly enjoyed the part. Whenever possible, he would arrange for meetings and classes to be held at his house rather than the university. The weekly postgraduate seminars run by the Victorian Studies Centre which I had been drafted in to help Philip run, always took place in his large comfortable study at home. It was a domestic stage, a set for a theatrical performance.

In contrast to Arthur's study with its projected image of a widely read, cultured and cultivated man, Philip's proclaimed itself the haunt of a modern academic specialist. Here, as near as possible, was every book, pamphlet, article and newspaper review published on Dickens, with runs of the relevant academic journals, and a comprehensive library of literary and historical studies of Victorian England. Philip was always turning in his chair to lift a particular book from the shelves in order to illustrate a point being made or to recommend it to students, or even to give or lend it to someone. And also, of course, to demonstrate how up to date he was with the latest thinking on the Master.

During a perfectly timed interval in the seminars, a couple of the female students would be firmly deputed to serve coffee and biscuits, and while this was being done Philip would disappear briefly back into the house. Sometimes he returned carrying in his arms his young son, bringing him on stage for a brief guest appearance. Business and home were thus blended together, with everyone at the seminar (staff, students, and visiting dignitaries) being granted honorary status as members of the extended family.

His love of the theatre, professional and amateur, was of long standing and one of the characteristics he shared with Dickens. It was something that he himself had brought to the relationship. Drama was, I think, probably dislodged as Philip's earliest area of scholarly expertise by his life-transforming discovery of Dickens which took place, as he himself always made clear, only when his university career was already under way. Once the connection was made, he happily embraced Dickens's own particular theatrical passions. He took an active part in the production and readings of plays in which Dickens himself had once appeared or was known to have admired, and put tremendous energy into recreating the dramatized public readings from his novels for which Dickens had been renowned. These performances took place at conferences; on tours of American universities; to undergraduate literary societies and book-reading circles; in theatres as well as in seminars and tutorials, and on television. It mattered nothing to him whether the audience was large or small, celebrated or obscure. He was enormously proud of the readings and totally sure that everyone he met would want to hear them.

One American academic visitor to the Victorian Studies Centre was honest and perhaps foolish enough to apologize effusively to Philip for having missed one of the public readings. He was instantly and pressingly assured that he needn't completely forgo the experience. Instead he could attend a rehearsal at Philip's home for a performance soon to be given abroad. He pleaded that he wouldn't think of intruding on such a private and psychologically important moment for the performer, but there was no way out. The event went ahead in Philip's study, with the visiting academic as the sole member of the audience. It must have been an extremely uncomfortable evening. For the visitor, but not for Philip. The performance was all that mattered to him, or rather the chance to give one, for he was quite incapable of letting any opportunity pass without leaping histrionically into action. And leaping is the activity I think of as most characteristic of him. It belongs to him as surely as it does to Harlequin. Never for one moment did he seem still.

He was for ever calling meetings, setting up agenda, ringing to clarify this or that point, making or changing arrangements. Nor was he shy about letting everyone know how busy he was. Semi-official letters and notes were dispatched endlessly from his desk, whether at home or the university. They were always handwritten. He had never mastered the mysteries of the typewriter and was not interested in doing so. A very un-Dickensian failure to keep up with the world, that! Nor had he learned to drive a car. Instead he racketed unsteadily about the campus on a bicycle. His dislike of cars was something I shared with him, but whereas it encouraged in me an already ingrained tendency to sit tight, it had the opposite effect on Philip.

A call asking him to speak about Dickens was all that was needed to set him going. As they could be in unlikely places and beyond the range of his bicycle, he relied on public transport to get him around, so an invitation to give a talk was capable of creating serious logistical problems. Whatever other business he had on hand, he would be constantly struggling with bus, train, or air timetables, painstakingly co-coordinating this or that connection or changeover.

On one occasion he discovered, at the very last minute, that he was double-booked, and asked me to help him out by giving one of the talks in his place. It was to an antiquarian society somewhere in the Potteries, not all that far from Leicester, but definitely out of the way. The venue turned out to be a small public library kept open late especially for the event. Philip gratefully supplied me with comprehensive travel directions. The journey involved several buses and trains, a taxi at one point, being picked up by a car at another, a restaurant dinner with members of the Society after my talk, and a stay over night in a country hotel. It might have been an itinerary compiled by John Le Carré. I devoted two whole days to fulfilling the engagement and ended up convinced of the rightness of my already established preference to have nothing to do with such invitations. Philip found this incomprehensible.

'You must fly the flag, Peter,' was the blustering advice he gave me. I replied that I could hardly be accused of not doing that. It was simply that I would rather do so by writing than by public lecture. Philip shook his head sadly over this attitude. Writing was all very well, and he himself always had a review, article or edition on hand. But the audience reached out to from a desk was distant and shadowy. It aroused insecurities in him. What he sought was the excitement of a public performance. I never actually heard him invoke 'the smell of the greasepaint, the roar of the crowd' but it would have been perfectly fitting for him to have done so.

When not dramatizing his relationship with Dickens he dramatized himself. Just as he was unable to remain seated for long in a seminar or tutorial, so, outside of the classroom, he was constantly moving, projecting himself in a variety of roles, asserting his personal happiness and fulfilment as a proud husband and father, dramatic reciter, a lecture-touring professor. He was capable of making himself quite unashamedly the principal topic of a conversation, striding in with outrageous opening gambits which he would offer in an apparently hesitant and reflective manner as though these were experiences which he'd been standing there long pondering before finally deciding they should be communicated. 'Have I ever told you that an American research student of mine heard Dermot Merrow, you know the holder of the Triple-Distinguished Chair of English Literature at Princeton, and author of that very good article 'Well, what *did* amuse Victoria, then?' say in one of his lectures that he thought my *Dickens and Crime* the best book ever written on Dickens?'

Inevitably it was said of him that at such moments he resembled one or other of Dickens's many pompous characters, though it was less often added as a qualifier that, like those same characters, he somehow managed to deflate the pomposity by disarming the reader/listener. The faults were venial, never vicious, and he himself was the only person to suffer from these particular performances. It was not so much vanity or snobbery that was being exposed, as disingenuousness.

I did not need to be informed by the departmental gossip factory about the affable nature of Philip's divorce, or how much he had longed to have children, or (a neat little detail here all set up for the sly comment it seemed destined to be) that the maiden name of the young student who became his second wife and the mother of those children was Dickins. A pity about the 'i' not being quite right, but there we are. All such personal information and a good deal more came to me quite unsought from Philip himself.

It was this openness that protected him from the type of sneaky denigration that had fixed itself so unreasonably to Arthur. Philip pre-empted himself from being treated in the same way. This still left plenty of material that could be used, but it was only the normal chatter of everyday university life. In this respect he fared no better or worse than any other academic who has the will and ability to establish a personal reputation by making a distinctive, worthwhile contribution to the understanding of his subject. Better perhaps, because Philip's larger than life outward manner placed his faults and weaknesses on display, presenting as sustenance for academic tittle-tattle only what he himself had left unsaid.

That was still enough to be mulled over by the small groups of academics, especially the young and the unestablished of whatever age, who were always to be found in staff coffee lounges or dining rooms; at the entrances or exits of formal meetings; propped up against corridor walls; in nooks and corners everywhere. Or gathered around suburban dinner tables where the wives could join in, though perhaps not so enthusiastically or freely as they were able to do at their own regular coffee mornings or in the 'tea clubs' as the more formally organized groups of academic wives were known in some universities.

Whatever the situation or setting, and pretty well regardless of the age, sex or status of the academic participants, it was quite certain they wouldn't be seriously considering the latest research by one of their more productive colleagues. Nor would they be seeking sympathetic advice on some theoretical or methodological problem they had run into with their own research, or sharing the excitement of having just discovered the work of an exciting new novelist or poet. They were far more likely to be running down those of their colleagues not present at that particular moment; denigrating the worth of any kind of personal achievement; explaining what they really would have liked to say in the recent staff or faculty meeting but hadn't dared to; deciding who was in and who was out; who wrote well and who didn't; who was moving up or moving where, and who was now never going to move at all; whose latest publication had finally demonstrated beyond doubt that he or she really didn't have a first-class mind, something that had, of course, been long suspected and was now finally settled. There they were gossiping away as though the very existence of their way of life depended on it. As, of course, it did. For a surprising number of them, there really was little else of such compelling interest.

In these various ways, there was revealed to me – unforeseen, unanticipated and totally unprepared for – the atmosphere in which my future career as a university teacher would take place. Although it was true, as I was frequently told, that my luck had been in when I landed up at Leicester, that lucky accident was still able to serve as a credible introduction to the larger academic world, at least within the Arts subjects with which I was concerned. Things were fundamentally much the same at friendly Leicester as they were at all those less attractive places elsewhere. The systemic diseases were just as rife, the sharp contrast between convinced superiority and actual mediocrity no less shocking.

Nor was it possible for my two professors to be regarded as unrepresentative, even though they would always rank high for me as being among the most considerate and decent of the breed I would ever meet. They were more or less effectively in charge, according to the strength of their respective personalities, imposing their individual wills where possible, but usually just keeping everything in check. They were not there to run things according to a set of objective standards or generally agreed values or knowledge, as anyone responsible for vocational or applied subjects would naturally be expected to do. English departments just aren't like that.

Essentially they are unruly gatherings of people of widely disparate talents, abilities, tastes and opinions who are supposedly united by their appreciation of one very special kind of artistic activity. But the truth of that supposition has long been in doubt. Nowadays the subject has become so fragmented that it no longer exists as a recognizable entity. What is communicated to students is knowledge or appreciation of those segments which individual tutors have managed to preserve, or are interested in promoting. By the mid-Seventies this was all beginning to be described quite openly and in perfectly good faith as a cafeteria system, an image that was apt all right but depressing to visualize. The student picks up a tray, joins the self-service line, is offered a large wedge of miscellaneous fiction, a helping of dramatic or poetic chips, and a choice of two or three tasty side dishes, all washed down with a cupful of Shakespeare. Tutors are there to devise and serve suitable portions and, when necessary, see that meals don't become too fatty or salty or sweet, while making sure that their own political, ideological, or theoretical views are represented somewhere or other on the syllabus. With these kitchen duties over for the day, they are left impressively free to pursue their personal scholarly or critical interests in whatever way, and of whatever standard, they can manage.

It is rampant individualism, irresistibly reminiscent of the Freudian id, that swirling mass of contradictions and antitheses in a state of permanent competition, all striving for attention without any synthesis or effective organization. 'All to pieces,' as Freud declares at one point. It's up to the ego to restrict the id's excesses, and that is exactly the function of the head of a department. He or she is the controlling ego (a super ego if the department is particularly fortunate) appointed to bring order to an otherwise unmanageable id. The tone and reliability of a department depends all but entirely on whatever qualities of personality or leadership can be mustered by whoever is in charge.

During the few years I spent at Leicester the governing moods bestowed on the department from above changed dramatically. Calm rationality gave way to brash sentimentalism, careful balance to fluctuating emotion, hidden self-questioning to blatant display, benign liberalism to unpredictable energy. The rest of the department continued as ever on its uncoordinated individualistic ways, adjusting to the change of tone with indifference or venom, but remaining essentially the same throng of contradictions, with wild disorder always somewhere around, whether in the open or held precariously at bay. And out of these unpropitious conditions, there does emerge, as Freud would not have been surprised to hear, good individual work. Some of it is original, much of it mundane and unimaginative but essential if the subject is to be maintained as a going concern. But a good deal of the individual research is hardly deserving of the name. It is of dubious value to even the researchers themselves and day by day becoming ever more meaningless and of little interest to anyone outside of Academia.

At the start of my entrance into this world for what was to be a period of twenty years it would still have been just recognizable as the one that Monica had entered a further twenty years back. As a product of the formative changes in higher education of the early Sixties it was impossible for me not to be aware that higher education was in a state of rapid change. Even so, I had no sense at the time of universities being caught up in a structural and educational upheaval so extreme that my memories of days at Leicester must now sound old-fashioned, and Monica's like ancient history. I certainly did not appreciate that the process of change, as we were both experiencing it at that moment, was ongoing, in fact had barely started. Nor could I possibly have known back then that virtually nobody, including university administrators and politicians, had any clearer idea than I did about what exactly was going on.

Perhaps the only thing I truly sensed was that whatever the nature of the larger changes taking place in universities, my own experiences could be seen in certain key ways as representative of them. And Monica? Well, in Leicester, back in the late 1960s, it would have been impossible for me to think of her as representative of anything.

* * * *

I don't know when I saw her again after that first staff meeting. Probably at another staff meeting a few weeks later, and then again at the one after that. It wouldn't have been a social occasion because I never did see Monica anywhere that could be thought of in those terms. She wasn't at any of the dinner parties given by individual members of the department to which I had been invited. Nor did she herself ever offer any hospitality to me or, as far as I'm aware, to anyone else. I was in and out of Philip's home all of the time, meeting visiting academics as well as people from other Leicester departments, but Monica was never there. The mere thought of her being even a temporary part of the jolly *Biedermeier* atmosphere of the Collins household is incongruous. But then, that would also be true in my experience of the more sedate home atmosphere of Arthur Humphreys and his wife. Of course Monica must, at some time or other, have been welcomed into both houses and it's only my narrow testimony that makes it seem otherwise. But even so, I soon came to understand that there was no university social activity, private or public, in which I could imagine her participating.

It seems likely, therefore, that if for some reason or other – restless nights, perhaps, or a shared preference for early morning tutorials – Monica and I hadn't both developed the habit of starting our working days with a cup of strong coffee I might have spent my four years at Leicester barely speaking to her. As it was, most of our meetings took place in a large comfortable coffee lounge that occupied a corner of the staff dining room, halfway up an attractive glass-fronted building that was one the university's more congenial architectural experiments.

Here, at about half-past nine in the morning, irregularly, entirely by chance and dwarfed by huge windows that skilfully trapped and contained the changeable Midlands weather, we would have coffee together. And talk. None of these encounters could ever have lasted for longer than about twenty minutes. We would sometimes be interrupted by colleagues or need to carry ourselves off early to prepare for the arrival of our tutees. I say we talked because that's a suitably neutral description, though really what took place were rarely more than brief exchanges, fragments, undeveloped opinions, at best the surprised discovery of shared interests. They were never pursued at length or explored in any depth or carried beyond the glass-enclosed coffee lounge.

The snippets of information about Monica that had drifted through to me didn't make a great deal of sense. The woman I knew from staff meetings was lively, opinionated, and sometimes very funny, yet it was said that in her private life she was reclusive, unknowable. Apparently she had a flat somewhere near the university to which she retired alone as soon as the day's official business was over. There, it was rumoured, she devoted herself to the bottle, or many bottles. Perhaps she did, perhaps she didn't. How could I know? She never seemed to me to be hung-over at half-past nine in the morning, though that needn't count for or against her. Here was another aspect of my new life that I was beginning to understand. After all, there can't be many better places to learn about alcoholism than university English departments. I never did hear much from Monica herself how she spent her evenings. The inadvertent clues which escaped from her were usually of a mundane nature and never particularly revealing, though they could be refreshingly uncomplicated.

About the radio especially, and though somewhat less, television as well. I would guess she took in quite a bit of one or other or both. Her taste was notably eclectic, covering a wide range of programmes – serial dramas, comedy, music, wrestling possibly, and boxing definitely.

'Did you hear it?' she spluttered at me over coffee one morning. 'Last night!'

I had heard it. A British heavyweight championship match broadcast live, a bruising, crude, thumping affair that had gone the full blood-spattered distance. Monica was delighted.

'What a going-over he gave him,' she gasped, jiggling in her seat, tugging her skirt as far towards her knees as it would go, and flashing her teeth at me. She was glowingly pleased, not just with the fight itself, but at finding someone to share retrospectively her brutal, and presumably solitary, pleasures of the previous evening.

That moment established a link between us. If there was a big fight in the offing she would try to catch my eye and make some kind of advance comment, usually in the slangy style she liked to affect at such moments. 'No problem for Frazier doing the business tonight, eh!' Or she would open her mouth wide, the scarlet lips framing her multi-coloured teeth, and, ignoring any company we might have been in, breathe across to me 'Ali' or 'Cooper' or 'Bugner' or the name of some other boxer who was currently up for glory or destruction. Then she would clamp her mouth shut and chortle through her teeth. No further words were needed, the extravagant mouthing having sufficiently indicated that someone was due for a good going-over.

My interest in boxing was extremely slight, little more than knowing what matches were in the offing. I don't suppose Monica's knowledge of it went any deeper, though perhaps knowledge is, anyway, the wrong word. She was an enthusiast, someone who, in a phrase of the day popularized by the great television comic actor Tony Hancock, 'enjoyed a good punch-up.' It was, I assumed, the atmosphere, the vicarious excitement that attracted her and sent her off the following morning to find someone with whom she could relive the experience.

Her manner of sharing, though, was unusual. It was never confessional, always careful not to move beyond the recounting of an immediate experience and barely personal at all, simply conveying the few skeletal facts or details without which any communication is impossible. If this suggests an extreme uneasiness or at best a retreat to the impersonal minimalist exchanges of everyday life, well Monica actually managed to avoid giving such an impression by being completely at ease with her self-imposed restrictions. And so was I, at ease with both her restrictions and my own growing inclination to treat academic company in rather the same cagey manner.

It was this wariness that we probably identified in each other. To her the manner was habitual, made natural by long practice. For me, self-protectiveness was new, still fresh and undeveloped, part of my gradual understanding that the world I had so recently landed up in was not one in which plain speaking or personal openness was valued or sensible. I would describe as one of my own characteristics an almost cold-blooded incuriosity about the private lives of casual acquaintances that borders on priggishness. My taste for gossip is so small that I have occasionally felt obliged to stop people from passing on to me a juicy revelation about someone known to both of us, or to walk away in mid-sentence. I truly don't care what most of the people I come across are doing when I'm not with them. It seems obvious to me that not wanting to know is quite a bit preferable to being nosy or slanderous, though I've met few academics who would agree with that. Indifference as an alternative creates its own problems. At best it tends to be regarded as an unendearing quality. In universities it is generally unacceptable.

It suited Monica, though. She was never driven to talk about her private life, and I didn't want her to. Nor did she care to know anything about mine. That probably goes some way to explaining why we got on well together and why I never did learn much about her. Down to the present day, my memories of her can seem curiously random, my knowledge frustratingly incomplete. And, just as she said little about herself, so neither of us said anything intrusive about other people in the department. Her occasional outbursts of bawdy indignation were hurled at distant figures: living politicians, dead writers, people in the news. I did notice that her allusions to contemporary writers could be casual to the point of familiarity. This I put down to the slightly disturbing habit, not uncommon among academics, of talking of famous writers, alive or dead, as though they were near relatives or friends of the family. If she referred at all to any of our colleagues it would be by means of a gargoyle-style grimace or a massive wordless sigh. Her lack of interest in the personal details of people around her was a match for mine, though in her case it would never have been taken for priggishness.

She obviously valued our meetings over early morning coffee and also, I imagine, the impersonal nature of our talk. Neither of us would have thought of ringing the other up or suggesting lunch or a drink together. That would have broken the terms of our undeclared contract. Nor was there any sexual element involved. No thought of it on mine. Nor, I'm certain, on hers. I expect she treated many other people in much the same manner, though 'people' there should probably read 'men' because I couldn't imagine her making up to a woman in this way.

And those other men would have been younger than her, as I was. This wasn't because she had a private taste for what in those days were yet to be labelled toy boys or anything remotely of the kind. In fact, I suspect she was drawn to younger men as a way of preserving her purity, an odd thing to claim, perhaps, for someone who dressed and spoke as she did. But then there was always something about her behaviour that was mysterious, that screamed out for an explanation you knew you were never going to get. Whatever the reason, she succeeded in establishing a strategy in friendships like ours that prevented her flamboyance and flirtatiousness from being misunderstood by the recipient. It was a skilful balancing act which allowed all the gusset-flashing, false eyelash fluttering, and constant body wriggling simply not to matter.

It always felt as though there was something hidden away inside her that was needed to complete the outward show. But it never emerged, not even enough of it to give a hint of what exactly it might be. Everything was squashed down, kept under or suppressed, every bit of it her own property. The hidden part was there all right, and she wanted you to know of its existence but without placing it on display. She took it with her, I assumed, when she retreated so decisively to her flat once the university day was over, and only linked together the private and public halves of her life during public spaces in the day, like staff meetings, coffee breaks or lunch.

The vital moments for her took place off campus, and no doubt they would have remained out of bounds, insubstantial fragments locked darkly away in her mysterious flat, if the rising sun hadn't driven her out to find someone to share them with. I'm aware this makes her sound vampiric, and the allusion is deliberate. Of course she spent the major part of her daylight hours not lying comatose in a lead-lined coffin but actively communicating with students, and successfully too apparently. Even so it came over, indirectly though powerfully, that her daytime experiences were relatively unimportant to her, nothing like as forceful as their equivalents in the hours of darkness. Only then, I used to imagine, did they flower into some kind of identifiable form or shape, an existence that she alone understood. The alternative on offer were evenings of an unremitting inactivity and dullness that simply didn't square with the morning Monica. My role was that of an uninitiated agent or catalyst, someone who was, as it were, well outside any overnight bloodletting and therefore safe.

This kind of mediating function had to be served by acquaintances rather than friends. I don't remember ever hearing of Monica as having a close friend of any kind, and I understood why. Friendship would have led inevitably to personal questions, an interest that could not be sent packing by a toothy splutter. Every morning she must have emerged from her flat, her head crammed with night-time images which she hawked about, waiting for someone to exorcise them for her, like the pulped, bloodied faces of the heavy-weight boxers that she carried to me and evoked while we were sipping our strong black coffee.

The solitary manner, the hideaway flat and vanishing act when the sun went down, might have gone largely unremarked, or at least dismissed as Monica's and nobody else's business – 'Well, that's what she's like. Let her get on with it. Why not?' – if they hadn't begun to impinge on parts of her life that were not simply her own. In fact, they were beginning to be thought of as out of harmony with university life, or, to put it rather more grandly, with the rapidly changing structure of higher education.

The academic year was divided roughly into seven months of teaching and five months of vacation which consisted approximately of one month at Christmas, one at Easter, three months in the summer. Although term-time and vacations were generally treated as distinct from each other, in theory they were one. As an undergraduate in the early Sixties, my tutors liked to insist that the long summer vacation especially was not to be confused with holidays. Holidays were the period of time in the summer when you backpacked to Turkey or set off to explore the new, burgeoning holiday resorts of southern Spain, while the vacation was an opportunity for unhurried study and reflection, a chance to absorb and expand your studies.

Although relatively few students followed the advice it could be imparted to them with appropriate solemnity because it also applied to the tutors themselves. They were expected to use their long vacation not to enjoy an extended holiday, but to carry out research and write articles and books. This was when they could make the contribution to the knowledge or understanding of their subject to which they were committed. All academics had signed contracts pledging themselves to precisely these activities and aspirations. The theory that the whole year, apart from those few weeks of clearly defined holiday, should be devoted to scholarly pursuits was agreed by everyone, however far individuals might fall short of the target.

Monica didn't even bother to take aim. Ignoring both ideal and reality she would leave Leicester as soon as possible after the official end of term to stay in a cottage she owned in Haydon Bridge, Northumberland, and not return to Leicester until the start of the next academic year. It wasn't a policy that need bring her inevitably into conflict with the university. She was entitled to stay wherever she wished during vacations, or any other time come to that. Many academics removed themselves to far more distant and exotic places than Haydon Bridge. Even so, her behaviour in this respect was a cause of friction in the department. It was beginning to test even Arthur's legendary tolerance, while Philip, in a state of perpetual motion, was pretty well incapable of understanding anyone who stood still for a few unnecessary minutes.

Monica had been at Leicester a long while. She had probably never taught at any other university. It was even possible that she was the only current member of the department who had been personally on hand to experience Arthur's embarrassing professorial inauguration. Whether or not, her earliest teaching experiences did date back to that time and it explained a lot about her attitude towards vacations. In those days her stubbornness might have been accepted as professional eccentricity: now it was untenable.

By the late Sixties, university expansion was bringing with it not only a rise in student numbers, better equipped universities, and new kinds of degree courses, but also a notable change in what it meant to be a university lecturer. This, like so much else that was going on in higher education seemed to have come upon academics as a surprise. No new terms of work were negotiated with the Association of University Teachers, no job descriptions drawn up, no plans presented to or discussed with the people most affected by the changes. Everything proceeded bit by unanticipated bit, with Academia's traditions being steadily eroded. Prominent among them was what at moments of particular irritation would be described proudly, and often pompously, as the ancient rights and privileges of academics.

Newcomers like me who had no previous standards by which they could measure their workloads barely noticed the changes, but more senior members of staff were seriously upset by them. Arthur must have looked back in amazement to the days when he himself had been expected to give a large proportion of the lectures and to run everything, helped only by a handful of permanent and part-time members of staff, one of whom may have been Monica. Now, much of his time was given to dividing up teaching and administrative responsibilities among some twenty full-time lecturers. The moment hadn't yet arrived when professors would be appointed not on the strength of any scholarly distinction they may have attained but because of their avowed willingness to construct syllabuses and chair committees, though it was observably on the way.

Of course Arthur had felt no resentment at handing over to Philip and returning to his own work. He had, actually, been doubly fortunate in having a successor who gloried in shouldering the additional duties. Otherwise, and apart from the change of departmental tone, it no longer mattered very much who was in charge. Whether handled with Augustan balance or Victorian brio, the head of department was unavoidably in the business of urging, cajoling or forcing the members of his team not simply to do more teaching, but to get them to take on this or that part of a fragmenting subject, undertake interviews, sit on one or other of the proliferating committees, attend faculty and department meetings, mark examination papers, interview prospective students, evaluate theses, make the tea and provide biscuits or store the sherry for the endlessly proliferating meetings. The once hallowed distinction between term and vacation was swiftly disappearing. Grudgingly or not, we all went along with the new conditions, except for Monica.

'No,' she would say. 'No, No. I will do everything asked of me during term, but the vacations are mine.'

And that was that. She was acknowledged to be a good teacher, a popular if rather flashy lecturer, and, as I was personally aware, a valuable contributor to discussions in staff meetings. None of this was any longer enough. Monica would take on extra work if she could carry it off to Haydon Bridge, but not if it meant her staying on in Leicester. There was no negotiation, no flexibility. A few days at the beginning or end of a vacation might be unavoidably surrendered, but no more. It explained the circumstances of my first meeting with her. That had been immediately before the official start of an academic year, and she had probably arrived straight from the railway station, dropped off at the university by private car or taxi. She couldn't have cut things any finer. There would have been tutorial groups to arrange, students to contact, reading lists to compile, the pre-term staff meeting itself to attend, and her flat to strew with earth in preparation for the new term.

This unwillingness of hers not to take part in administrative chores that intruded on her vacation wasn't the whole problem. After all, not many of us did actually enjoy taking on extra administrative duties, and she would have been widely forgiven for adopting a policy of passive resistance on the matter. The larger objection was that during the vacations she refused to do any work at all that might be called academic except read, and reading was beginning not to count unless it could be shown to be of a suitably productive kind. Monica wasn't working on a book, or writing an article, or even reviewing the work of others. That level of inactivity was bad enough. Worse was her refusal to even pretend she was engaged in any of the approved activities.

I don't remember her ever claiming that vacation reading was appropriate academic work, but she might well have done and, in one sense, reasonably so. In the early days of her career the principal responsibility of university lecturers was assumed to be their own intellectual development. This, so the theory ran, benefited them personally, and thus their subject, department, and university. They were setting standards, leading the way. It didn't mean that the academics who had been active in the early years of the twentieth century weren't expected to write as well as read. Very far from it! They had actually created and established, consciously and purposefully, English as a respectable area of academic study. But it did mean there was no hurry for them to move from the one activity to the other. If they were driven by ambition it was of a personal rather than a departmental kind. In the tiny departments of those days which were dominated by one established professor, it wouldn't have been unacceptable for a young assistant lecturer to dispense with glory and settle instead for personal development and teaching.

Monica wasn't, of course, alone in feeling pressured by the changing pattern of university workloads. It was affecting every one of us and our responses varied, but how we responded was beginning to matter a good deal because those personal decisions were creating fault lines of a new kind. University departments now had introduced into them additional reasons for tension and, consequently, fresh resentments to be whispered about.

Those academics who were actively dedicated to making something of their personal research, took on board whatever extra departmental work they were called upon to do. They grumbled a bit but still got on with their own work. A significant number, though, followed Monica's line in trying to live according to a model handed down from more leisurely academic days. They differed from her only in being less honest or sometimes more openly manipulative. They would go out of their way to make it known in public how much of their vacations they had spent slaving away in an acceptably academic manner or how they had managed to put in a bit more work on the big scholarly project that occupied all their spare moments. These undertakings may well have been genuine attempts to gather together the scattered remnants of once treasured ideals. But all too often the will was gone and the motive lost for ever. There was also a certain amount of conscious deviousness at work, with large much touted academic enterprises that were never truly intended to reach completion at all but were kept continuously in process like Penelope's web, though not justified by her loving ways and stern moral values.

New balms for a guilty academic conscience were also becoming available. As with all growing empires, higher education was in need of more and more administrators to do the work that it had itself created. For those academics who, for whatever reason, were not unhappy to give up on research, here was a respectable way out of their personal dilemmas. They would maintain their teaching commitments, drop any pretence of research, and undertake more administrative work. Such decisions were not taken necessarily in a cynical spirit. After all, the jobs were for everyone's benefit and someone had to do them. But they could still provoke from colleagues angry mutterings of skiving and dishonesty, of defections and betrayal. A split developed in departments between 'researchers' (who did the teaching allotted to them but also had reputations as published writers and were therefore productive) and 'teachers' (who similarly carried out their teaching duties, but who wrote and published very little, if anything at all, and were therefore unproductive). Everything about the conflict was fraught with potential trouble. It involved the nature of university research and teaching, the concept of academic freedom, contractual obligations, and not least the grounds for promotion within departments.

Monica cared about none of this. She was a committed teacher and an equally committed non-researcher who refused to cooperate with administrative duties unless they conformed with her personal timetable. Nor would she become involved in any kind of writing. During a conversation with her in which she had disclosed a warm appreciation of the work of some barely remembered writer, I suggested that she put her ideas down on paper. An article, perhaps, or a review.

'Oh no,' she said, slightly shocked as though I was being indelicate. 'No, no. I don't do anything like that.'

And because she didn't do anything remotely like that she was coming to be regarded as someone who wasn't pulling her weight, or, in the more legalistic taunt that was now increasingly in play, as someone who was not fulfilling the terms of her contract. It began to be hinted that Monica was an encumbrance, a burden, someone who was being carried. She was aware of this, resented it, and went on as she always had done. The treasured principle of academic freedom meant that she couldn't be dismissed for her recalcitrance. She was probably penalized, though, by being denied the promotion that she would have expected to come to her automatically after a given number of years teaching. This meant that her salary would be held at a fixed point on the scale, at 'the bar' as it was known.

On all of these issues I was as different from Monica as it was possible to be. I belonged with those academics for whom term and vacation were barely separable. The only difference was that for seven months of the year there were students around who needed to be taught, and for five months there weren't. The time given to teaching and research were automatically adjusted. Although no one was likely to accuse me of not fulfilling the terms of my contract, that wasn't enough to prevent me from becoming an immediate target for disparaging comments. I was an obvious target for the snipers: it could even be said that I had set myself up for them. I was a disruptive element because I was busily doing exactly what I wanted to do, and what I had so wrongly assumed, before arriving at Leicester, most other people in the same job as myself would also be doing.

I had published my first book, a short critical study of George Gissing's *New Grub Street*, just before I arrived at Leicester. This was followed during my first year there by an edition of *A Child of the Jago*, together with a biographical study of its author Arthur Morrison. The research for it had been done while I was a postgraduate student and carried with me from Sussex to Leicester. It was the first stage of my work on the portrayal of working-class life in Victorian fiction which also began to be published while I was at Leicester. The revelations about Morrison aroused an interest both inside and outside Academia, with reviews in national newspapers and discussions and interviews on the radio. The publishers, who were as surprised as everyone else by the book's enthusiastic reception, hurried to produce a second edition and supported it with newspaper advertisements drawing attention to the edition's originality.

I would eventually learn that almost any kind of extramural attention is distrusted by most academics, but back then I was astonished at the resentment the favourable reception of this early work of mine provoked in some of my colleagues. Whatever originality or value the work itself may have had was of no interest to them. The only motive for it they were capable of seeing was personal ambition. I had announced myself not as someone obsessively involved in writing and research, but as a rival all set to speed ahead of them in the promotion stakes. It was my first experience of the small-mindedness endemic in English departments, and the shock was intense. At first I tried to explain it away in terms of my inexperience or naivety, which in some senses it was, but this mood was quickly transformed into a resentment of my own. I knew pretty well from the start that I was no threat to them of any kind they were capable of understanding, and that therefore I had little to fear from their misguided calculations. But there was no way these feelings could be communicated, or indeed any reason why they should be. As I had no intention of changing my priorities, the tension was likely to remain and I began consciously to consider some kind of defence strategy to deal with it.

Outright escape was something I was already beginning to contemplate with pleasure. But although that would be the most complete and satisfying answer, it could only be something for the indeterminate future. As I considered what to do immediately, a comparison of my circumstances with Monica's revealed how intractable things were. She was regarded as not doing enough, I was seen as hyperactive. She was resented for not publishing anything, me for publishing too much. She had no ambition, I was obviously on the make. I was quickly learning not only about the petty nature of much academic life but its fundamental conformity and unadventurousness as well.

A few more years of university teaching and I myself would be openly critical of academics in Monica's position, but not then. Although it was plain enough how much some of my colleagues were determined to get away with, I didn't readily place Monica in their company. Nor did it matter that as far as the researcher/teacher divide was concerned Monica and I were on opposite sides because we were both, in our different ways, set apart from so much that the department represented. Nowadays I'm inclined to believe that the quality we had most in common was a lack of interest in academic status. That was enough, and sufficiently open to aggressive misunderstanding, to make temporary friends of us and, perhaps, to give me glimpse of a possible way ahead for me. Not that either us would have thought of raising so personal an issue. We were anyway discovering other shared interests and values which were quite a bit it more personally absorbing than boxing. Minor fiction, for a start.

* * * *

In those days, most university teachers of English literature were wary of letting it be known that they read anything but a carefully prescribed list of authors and texts. If they didn't actually submit themselves to the tyranny of an *Index Librorum Prohibitorum*, it was because they didn't need to. Although in essence a voluntary system, it was powerfully enforced by the fear of losing prestige if it should become known that they enjoyed reading any but the most approved of authors. Many of them were just beginning to think that they might risk admitting to a taste for Dickens, and were still waiting for permission to reopen their dust-covered volumes of Milton.

At its most extreme this doctrinal narrowness was defended as an essential guardianship of high cultural standards, though for disbelievers it looked more like a masquerade of fake sensitivities. Few people would have dared predict its imminent collapse, yet ten years on and it had pretty well disappeared. My personal objection to it lay not in the literary standards it espoused, but in the way its aggressively anti-historical stance denied the validity of any approach to the study of literature other than its own. I was not alone in my opposition. At Leicester, Philip Collins, and the Victorian Studies Centre generally, were of much the same mind, and offered an atmosphere in which I felt at home, though to many people Philip and I were both mavericks. The Victorian Studies Centre operated solely at a postgraduate level and in this respect was not characteristic of the English department as a whole.

But Monica, for reasons that had nothing to do with Victorian Studies, was fully sympathetic.

She had her own distinctive manner of deriding our colleagues' conviction that fine taste was a matter of adherence to a narrow literary canon. She developed ways of mocking them that they seemed incapable of understanding or perhaps even recognizing. Knowing they were liable to become faint at the thought of anyone admitting to having read, say, the novels of Charles Kingsley, she would announce in her spluttering and spitting manner.

'Well of course *Charles* Kingsley is all right, but I don't really know why people make such a fuss about him. It's his brother Henry they ought to be paying attention to. *Ravenshoe!* Have you read that? That's the Kingsley to get your teeth into.'

Ravenshoe typified her general fondness for adventure tales and romantic excess. R.D.Blackmore's *Lorna Doone* was another of her favourites in this 'have you read?' game, along with the whole of Sir Walter Scott. Not that her taste was restricted to the minor or neglected. It was impressively varied and unpredictable. D.H.Lawrence, an officially approved author, she read and chortled over in a rather timeless New Womanish sort of way. She was also very enthusiastic about the poetry of George Crabbe which few people read. Coleridge was another favourite. Most academics read his poetry all right, though selectively. Monica went for all of it. And though she enjoyed flaunting the element of shock in her broad literary taste, it had its influential side as well. The first and second year syllabuses at Leicester allowed for lectures on a wide range of authors from the eighteenth to the early twentieth century, and Monica not only argued for her unfashionable favourites to be included but lectured enthusiastically on them. I never remember any students at Leicester opting to read Scott's novels for my tutorials, though they could have done. That Scott was on the syllabus was because Monica insisted it would be ridiculous to have an introductory course of nineteenth-century literature without him. At the same time, she also admired Yeats – the most orthodox, totally acceptable academic literary taste it was possible for anyone to have – yet was no less admiring of

Hardy's poetry which was just being dragged in from the cold and still not widely appreciated in academic circles.

Neither of us read widely out of a desire to be provocative. Monica seemed to be driven by a compulsive need for books and the common-sense belief that critical judgments were only worthwhile if they were based on extensive reading. 'How does he *know*?' she asked me, wide-eyed with mock horror, responding to my tale of a colleague, hostile to the whole idea of a Victorian Studies Centre, who had informed me that there was little English poetry worth reading between Keats and Yeats. It wasn't the judgment as such that shocked her, but the ignorance on which the judgment was so obviously based. My own wider reading had something of the same compulsive curiosity that drove Monica. But it was also more compartmentalized than hers, and governed by the kind of literary history I was trying to develop. This was a professional decision, and not at all the same thing as my personal literary preferences which were in fact as 'high' as those of any supporter of a narrow literary canon, or as Philip, jocularly and not unfairly, liked to dub them, Arnoldian.

Flirtation with minor literature, though, was a precarious game to play in the tetchy literary atmosphere of the time. The historical concerns that made it necessary for me to develop an understanding of an unusually wide range of fiction was often taken to mean that my own critical standards were essentially set apart from those held by my more orthodox colleagues. They were actually nothing of the sort. Monica's common sense was similarly open to misunderstanding. 'Of course, I'm not saying that Mark Rutherford *is* D.H.Lawrence, but...' she would say, knowing full well that it would be generally accepted that that was exactly what she was claiming. As she was not bound by my kind of historical consideration and was never entirely able to suppress the shock tactics she was so good at, there was sometimes a blurring in her literary preferences that I couldn't share. There was a bit of teasing in all of this, but she was certainly not out to make a cult of philistinism. Nor did she feel a need to offer any kind of self-justification for what others might consider literary perversity. She knew perfectly well that reliance on a narrow literary canon to justify one's professional existence was no more respectable than her apparent randomness. Her taste for unfashionable literature was perfectly genuine and deeply lodged in personal experience. She really did seem to have read everything, and although her response could sometimes be over-emotional, it also allowed her to display a genuine feel for certain strikingly individual books that are much-loved by lay readers but tend to be treated warily by the higher criticism.

When I told her I had signed a contract with Penguin to edit *Cranford* and *Cousin Phillis* she was delighted. At one time or another she had, of course, read all of Elizabeth, or 'Mrs' Gaskell as both of us, along with almost everyone else in those unreconstructed days, would have called her. *Sylvia's Lovers* was one of the historical adventure tales that Monica was constantly urging people to read. But, once we had explored the byways of Gaskell's varied works, it was *Cranford* to which she returned, even though in doing so, as she admitted, she had to be prepared to accept the tears that inevitably accompanied the reading. It was far too 'sad' a book for her to pick up often. Miss Matty's situation is one of the 'saddest' in the whole of literature, she would say, her eyes clouding at the mere thought of the inner suffering of Mrs Gaskell's seemingly fragile heroine.

We discussed the highly allusive nature of *Cranford* as one of the qualities that allowed it to appeal to the scholarly as well as the general reader, and the ways in which this made it a challenging task to edit. I told her that although I would be only the latest in a very long line of *Cranford* editors, I hoped to make my edition one of the most thoroughly annotated ever. 'That's something to look forward to,' she said, and I responded to her warmth by making a mental note that I would put Monica's name on my list of people to be sent complimentary copies when the book did eventually materialize.

While boxing established a jokey connection between us and literature provided the staple topic of our conversations, they were both sidelined by the discovery that we shared an enthusiasm for jazz. Some fifteen years earlier this particular musical taste of ours would have been widespread in university circles, but no longer. I was not aware of many people at Leicester being interested in jazz, and there was no reason why anyone should have known of my long personal involvement with it.

I gave up playing the trumpet when the University of Sussex offered me a place under regulations governing mature students. I qualified in this way because I had reached the 'mature' age of twenty three, and I stopped playing in order to concentrate fully on my studies. The decision was never regretted and in no danger of being reversed. If I had had any doubts, they would anyway have been eased by the jazz scene largely giving up on enthusiastic semi-pros like me. It proved to be an unstoppable process and by the time I was at Leicester traditional jazz was well on its way to becoming a culturally peripheral, minority interest. Some Traddy-Pop, as it was now scornfully known, was still to be found in the eclectic hit parade of the later Sixties, but live traditional jazz had become a desolate, beleaguered experience. Jazz Clubs were closing down while student dances at universities and art schools which had once featured traditional jazz bands were rapidly changing to rock and pop. Jazz also now held a less prominent, entirely private place in my life, and there was no reason for anyone in the department to have known of my interest in it unless prompted by something said in passing. This was how, with Monica saying gruffly that 'Auden's *blues*, don't sound much like *blues* to me,' that I came to tell her that I had once played the trumpet in a jazz band.

She was immediately interested, full of relevant questions. What kind of band was it? Had I been a pro? Where did I play? Who with? Had I ever met this or that musician? With these questions answered, more followed, making it clear that Monica knew what she was talking about. For a few moments she was eager for details. Had we played King Oliver and Louis Armstrong numbers? 'Goodness isn't *Riverside Blues* the most beautiful thing?' Did I like Sidney Bechet? And what about Bessie Smith? And the Chicagoans, Eddie Condon, Max Kaminsky and Bud Freeman? And Pee Wee Russell? Did I like him? Wasn't he something rather special? I responded much as I would do when we were swopping titles by lesser-known novelists and poets.

Oliver and Armstrong, most certainly. Theirs had been precisely the kind of music we had dreamed vainly of being able to play. I was undecided about Bechet, and always had been. Not enough of an ensemble man, I suppose. As for the white Chicagoans, no, not really. Good fun for a while, but not really for me. Monica listened intently, happy with my positive responses, ignoring without comment anyone I seemed not to be enthusiastic about, and challenging nothing, a stance she would never have countenanced had the name of, say, Thackeray or Clough cropped up. It was *my* experiences she wanted to hear about. There was no attempt to match them with any of her own. Question and answer was the right approach. She was satisfied with that, delighted to have discovered this side of me and eager to swop names and tune titles.

Jazz now became a major point of reference between us, though we never behaved together the way true fans tended to, swopping experiences and memories of the first time we had heard favourite artists or recalling fondly where we first came across this or that number. Nor did Monica ever speak of buying or owning records. The music she enthused about seemed to come to her mainly from the radio. If I knew the record or musician she mentioned I'd happily talk about it with her. But there were times when I was conscious of being considerably less currently informed than her about new releases and developments. Not that she appeared to find this a deficiency in me. Nor did she ever seem to be seeking from me particular responses or judgments. She was content with bringing into the morning light her solitary nocturnal experiences of listening to jazz, communicated in the same way as the thrill of a boxing match. It was the human contact after the experience itself that seemed to matter to her, the having someone there to mention it to.

On one occasion, and it must have been in the second half of May 1970, she carried with her to the coffee lounge an unfamiliar air of urgency. She was distressed, clearly relieved to see me.

She said, 'It's terrible news about Bunny, isn't it? I thought I might have seen you before this. You're the only person here who'd understand. Who else would care?'

Her faith in me was entirely misplaced. I didn't have the faintest idea what she was talking about.

I asked, hesitatingly, 'Bunny?'

'Bunny,' she confirmed, adding as explanation, 'Rabbit. Hodges. Johnny Hodges. To go in such a way at sixty two. That's all he was. It's terrible.'

She didn't realize that I hadn't understood her, but accepted my blankness as confusion over the nickname she had used. For me the hesitation was welcome because this was the first I had heard of the death of Johnny Hodges. That, no doubt, was because I rarely read newspapers. There's something about them I've never quite trusted, and usually I prefer to learn about current affairs from late-night television. Now and then I feel obliged to look into a newspaper, even to buy one, but there are months on end when I'm quite happy to leave them alone. This would have been one of my newspaperless spells.

Even so, in those rock-and-pop infested days, it wasn't at all certain that the press would have given much attention to the death of one of the greatest alto saxophonists in the history of jazz, an indispensable contributor to the Duke Ellington sound, and the leader of memorable session groups made up largely of Ellington sidemen. Some of the classier papers might have carried obituaries, but not the rest, and the news hadn't been on whatever television I was watching at the time. But even if I had known, I still wouldn't have been able to respond appropriately. I had liked Hodges's work without feeling any great attachment to it. In the past my interest in jazz had been narrow. I had never moved far enough away from revivalism to embrace with any depth of feeling the vast middle ground of jazz that was here represented by Johnny Hodges and the Duke Ellington Orchestra. Monica clearly had and she was distraught.

Although this seemed to indicate that her preferences in jazz were broader than mine and not governed (as mine tended to be) by contentedly retreating back in time, they were still rooted in the past. For both of us the modern revolution in jazz was an impassable barrier, a cut-off point beyond which neither of us ever thought of straying. The leading figures in modern jazz she would refer to contemptuously as disjunctive and formless, a denial of historical links and past greatness.

'It's not jazz.' She would proclaim sternly. 'Not really. No harmony. No swing. No *blues*. What does it have?' Then, with a characteristic shift from gloom to chomping humour. 'Or *rather*, what does it have that *we* could possibly *want!*'

I had no wish to contest such views. Even so, the death of Johnny Hodges raised differences between us that felt substantial. It came down to personal responses. Mine were conventional, adequately expressed by bidding a respectful farewell to a musician whose undeniable greatness had never been for me a prominent jazz experience. That would have been insufficient for Monica. She clearly regarded Hodges as central and had taken the news of his death as a serious shock, the feeling she communicated being akin to personal mourning. It convinced me that I must have underestimated both the nature and the depth of her tastes in jazz. All the more reason for me to be as positive as I could to someone who was looking to me for sympathy in her loss.

And that sense of loss, for all dedicated jazz fans, was becoming a regular experience. Most of the great early musicians were already dead. Now, their immediate successors, who were not only recording legends but had become more personally known as near contemporary performers as well, were gradually going. Monica was intensely aware of these deaths. Her valedictory line on Johnny Hodges was that he was far more than merely a great individual artist. He represented a form of jazz that had built on and refined its New Orleans and Chicago foundations, creating the new while maintaining close links with older traditions. Whether the same could be said of the yet younger generation of musicians who were set to follow him was highly doubtful. In what I knew of recent trends in jazz, continuity was something distrusted rather than admired. It therefore made good sense that to Monica there could be no possible replacement for a musician like Hodges with his exquisite melodic line and blues-inspired phrasing. How could there be? She was right to believe I would understand, but I was still surprised by the personal depth, the sadness, the bitterness even, of her response.

'It's all going,' she said. 'It's ending, isn't it?'

She was looking to me for some kind of consolation that I don't suppose for one minute she really believed I could offer. Her powdery face was forlorn, weary, and her voice clear and sad, with none of its usual irreverent crackle. I was concerned by her distress. Not that it was unreasonable to mourn a great artist. Far from it. It was the comprehensiveness of her gloom that I couldn't grasp. But it clearly wasn't a suitable moment to open that kind of issue. Confronted with Monica's doleful conviction that 'everything was going,' and annoyed by my own inadequate response to her sorrow, all I could think of doing was to invoke the still living presence of the greatest of all jazz musicians.

'Well,' I said. 'Louis is still around. So it can't be all over just yet. I think we should wait until he goes before pulling the curtain.'

She was pleased with these easy words. At least they cheered her up sufficiently for her shoulders to rise and her head bounce forward to deliver a classic broad-mouthed grimace.

'Oh yes,' she agreed. 'That's true enough. It's not over as long as Satchmo's about.'

The reprieve she was happy to welcome lasted for little more than a year. Louis Armstrong died on 6 July 1971. He had been in every way a more revolutionary artist than Johnny Hodges, an infinitely more influential figure in the history of jazz, far better known, and popular in a wider sense as well. He had recently had a handful of sentimental, predominantly vocal recordings high in the hit parade. His face and voice were iconic. He had appeared in films, and sung with some of the great figures of American entertainment. He had even to some extent breached America's vicious racism by performing with major white showbiz figures like Bing Crosby and Frank Sinatra who had made it unashamedly clear that they revered him. For every jazz fan who mourned the trumpeter who can be quite reasonably described as the most original musician of the twentieth century there were thousands of other people who simply loved the sound of the man's voice, his infectious smile and cheery philosophy, his actual being. There was no way the media would not want to give maximum coverage to the passing of this particular jazzman.

I heard of his death on the early evening radio news. I was getting ready to go out to dinner. Half-dressed, I sat on the stairs leading down from the bedroom to the hall and cried. It is always said that people of my generation remember where they were when they heard the news of President Kennedy's assassination, and, that's certainly so for me. I do remember exactly where I was at that moment, and how I heard and felt about the news. But I will also never forget where I was when I heard of the death of Louis Armstrong or how much greater was the emotional impact of his death compared with that of his president eight years earlier. Louis I regarded then, and still do, as by far the greater American of the two. And the more serious loss. Kennedy was instantly replaced by a man who was less charismatic but probably just as effective a president. Armstrong remains for ever irreplaceable.

The following morning Monica joined me for coffee. Term was recently over and she was probably still around with the rest of us only to help tidy up after Finals. I expect we had been looking out for each other, though I can remember little of our talk. I suspect that not much was said. We were there not to talk but to be together. 'Who else would understand?' Who indeed?

Monica broke the silence between us. 'You said he'd be the next to go,' she announced. There was nothing accusatory in her tone. She was simply acknowledging in a flat, tired voice that I had been right. It was like being awarded an Orphic crown, though one that was hardly deserved because I hadn't actually said anything of the sort. Perhaps she was misremembering my words. More likely, it was something she wanted to believe. I had delayed her mourning process, made her wait a little longer. Now Hodges and Armstrong – Rabbit and Satchmo – were united in death, and, given her known views on jazz history, she was free to predict that very soon the whole game would be over, all human links between legendary live performance and recorded evidence gone for ever. It was as much as she could bear. What she appeared to want from me was some kind of confirmation, but disbelief and certainty jangled so discordantly together in her that she was incapable of voicing what exactly it was she expected. There was little I could say. Louis

Armstrong's survival had been my reassurance on the last occasion. Now he had gone and there were no other equivalent jazz icons from the past to offer up to console Monica's distress.

There remains for me something suitably final about that meeting. Although I was to spend a further year at Leicester it was the last time I remember being with Monica. Perhaps the melancholy nature of our response to Armstrong's death has obliterated lots of subsequent coffee mornings. Maybe there were no further meetings between us. Actually, I've no certain idea, taking all in all the four years we knew each other, how many meetings over coffee there were.

Not that the number matters. Whether few or many, they don't link up in any purposeful way to create a defining focus. They exist as a series of separate highlights, and that's fair enough because the only certain thing about all of this is that there was no continuity whatsoever in my friendship with Monica. Was it even a friendship? Well yes, but a limited one. We came together fortuitously, and we parted without even saying goodbye to each other. I liked her and enjoyed her company and talk. It's therefore tempting to claim a special kind of relaxation together that wasn't easily on offer from most other people in the department, but I'm not sure if even that is really true.

Lots of fragments, bits and pieces, thrown arbitrarily together, that's what it was. Nor did I have then, or have yet, the slightest idea of the nature of Monica's possible friendships with our immediate colleagues. Common sense insists that some of them must have been more substantial than ours. The much longer time she had known them would be enough to ensure that. But I'll hang on to the conviction that there wouldn't have been one truly close or confidential friend among all of them, no one who had ever truly penetrated the spooky inner sanctum after sunset. And anyway, for me at least, the main issue lies elsewhere, slightly aslant of any negotiations about who might have known the most about Monica. I can bring it into focus by trying to recall other women I knew spasmodically or occasionally, much as I knew Monica, not well or intimately I don't mean, but as part of university life in those years as Leicester moved from the late Sixties into the early Seventies.

I can visualize some of them, bring them back to my mind, and place them in certain defining events or occasions. But there's no desire to push my memory further, to learn more about who they were or what they were like.

Why then shouldn't a similar kind of amnesia apply to Monica? Why is it that I remember so much more about her? And the truth is, I don't. Remembering her has been forced upon me. Not against my will, but in spite of it. Every aspect of our friendship has the power to carry a significance beyond itself. That's why I feel it to be important for me to be punctilious in fixing precise details while at the same time admitting that I can't be sure I have recalled these events accurately. With most people this simply wouldn't matter. But with Monica my memories and assumptions can be tested, challenged, judged. With her, I had my one brush with true literary genius. It was oblique, unsought, almost totally unrealized at the time, and it remained undeveloped. But real, definitely real.

There are, or will be, people out there who may read this and will never have heard of me and weren't anywhere about when Monica and I were sipping coffee and talking, but who, nonetheless, will feel themselves free to contradict what I've said. It's quite possible they'll tell me that I've got Monica all wrong and therefore myself as well. That's not fair. Of course it's not, but it's the way things are. Biographical spies, professional inquisitors, are already hanging around in the wings with their lie detectors and recorders plugged in, waiting for a suitable moment to enter and pronounce. Not watching out for me. Oh no. It's what Monica did or thought, or didn't do or think, that will sooner or later become of urgent concern to people who have had no personal experience whatsoever of her or of me. In effect they will be picking up on my own problem. They're the reason why she hasn't slipped casually out of my memory, why I can't help trying to remember whatever I can.

One morning, and here I have to admit that I'm not sure when exactly, though I guess it would have been about halfway through my four-year spell at Leicester, so, let's say between the deaths of Johnny Hodges and Louis Armstrong, we talked casually of the tutorials we were on our way to take. Mine was on Hardy.

'Well, lucky you,' Monica sighed. Her response was unusually warm, emotionally charged. She said something about there being times when our jobs really did seem to be the most privileged in the world. It was unusual for her to talk of what we did as special in any way, or to mention her teaching at all. It was something accepted as there to be done: well and efficiently no doubt, but essentially an adjunct to other parts of life. Exceptionally, on this particular morning, the thought of sharing with a group of students 'the melancholy...the beauty...the overwhelming sadness' of Hardy's poetry was powerful enough to undermine her customary reticence.

I said it was Hardy's novels I would be discussing later that morning, but, not wishing to deflate her romanticism, I tried to keep the subject where she had clearly wanted it to go. It didn't seem to me that students found much to interest them in Hardy's poetry, and that this was true of quite a bit of the literature we expected young people to read, understand and discuss. Even when they were up to the literary challenge, they often weren't emotionally prepared for it. Though once I had said this I began immediately to wonder whether our syllabus did actually give any attention at all to Hardy's poetry. The novels were securely there, but the poetry? Monica took up my query without it even being voiced.

'Quite,' she said, fluttering her arms about and nodding her head as though in vigorous agreement but at the same time speaking reflectively and shifting the issue away from the students. 'They see it as too simple, don't they? It's all too much to the point for this lot here. They think only the difficult is real, when in fact that's the only thing they are capable of teaching.' She gave another wave of her arms, embracing this time those of our Leicester colleagues who had driven simplicity from the literary canon, scornfully dismissing it as unfit for their over-complicated minds.

Then, in the same dreamy mood, she said, 'Of course, Philip thinks that Hardy is the best of all modern English poets. *The* best.' Enhancing her enjoyment with a throaty parodic chortle, she added in a deeper voice. 'Beside whom...and all that.'

'Philip does?' I replied, surprised to hear this of a colleague whose literary tastes I thought I knew pretty well. Yet here I was totally unaware that Hardy's poetry mattered so much to him.

My surprise set Monica giggling.

'*My* Philip,' she said with exaggerated clarity. 'Not *your* Philip, *my* Philip.'

Well, my Philip was Professor Collins, the Dickens specialist who had recently become head of the English department. No problem about that. But who on earth was her Philip?

The possessive note in her voice had been unavoidable, and I was pleased to hear it, a little condescendingly so as well, I imagine. My immediate response was to think how good it was to learn that her personal life wasn't as empty as I had always assumed it to be. She wasn't, after all, a lost creature of the night. Not only was there someone in her life, but someone very special if the pride with which she had delivered his name was to be trusted. Unfortunately I had no idea who her Philip was and I could hardly ask her straight out to reveal his identity. How could I, after knowing her for so long? Still, the information shouldn't be difficult to obtain. Monica had assumed it was already in my possession, and that probably meant that it *was* in most other people's. I needed a suitably knowledgeable and innocent source, and I knew at once where to find it. Some two years had now passed since my shocked initiation into academic rivalry and I had learned from that experience. My earlier naivety (if that was what it had been) was gradually hardening into a general wariness over who to trust and not to trust that was keeping me increasingly aloof from daily academic chatter. That consciously distanced side of my personality had just let me down with Monica. Now, it could be turned to my advantage.

I settled on someone a few years senior to me who was moving steadfastly and conscientiously up the academic ladder. Aware that neither writing nor research was likely to bring him the position he longed for, he had decided on a different path to academic advancement. Step by step, precarious handhold by precarious handhold, he was desperately ingratiating himself with anyone who might be able to help him on his way to a Chair. Any Chair, anywhere in Britain, would do. His ambition was entirely naked in that everyone seemed aware of it, though the strategy was unusual. In my experience, ingratiation has little to commend it as a means to academic advancement, and is not found very often among academics. In a world where true individuality really is ultimately all that matters and is in surprisingly meagre supply, ingratiation is too embarrassingly visible. It can also go seriously wrong. To succeed it has to be applied with the manic deviousness of an Iago, but that's rare, and, given the rewards offered by universities in terms of status and money, hardly worth the effort. In Academia would-be Iagos tend to end up as Uriah Heeps.

From the moment I arrived in Leicester Dr Ingratiate-desperate-for-a-Chair had been prominent among those people who had set me down as a dangerous rival. I wasn't a focus for his customary fawning manner because I had no power that might further his ambitions. That, surely, should have eased his worries, but it simply made things worse. He was incapable of seeing in me anything but the ability to beat him in the race to a professorship. It was a fear that possessed and completely unsettled him. He was constantly trying to belittle my standing in the department by sly, underhand comments. But that wasn't enough for him. So misguided were Dr Ingratiate's fantasies that he himself undermined them by a compulsive need to let me know, in some private way or another, what he was up to.

Shortly after the publication of my edition of *A Child of the Jago*, at a time when I had been at Leicester for something less than a year, I was walking across the campus when there was the sound of light running footsteps behind me. Before I could turn round, a familiar voice at my shoulder muttered in a giggling whisper, 'You're after a Chair. That's what you're after, aren't you?'

If Dr Ingratiate had paused for a moment instead of skipping away, Puck-like, thrilled with his own cleverness, I could have given him an answer that would have calmed his fears and made him a contented man. I was in a position to assure him that I was determined never to be in competition with him or anyone else for any Chair. My one year's experience of university life had been enough for me to reach that decision. A bit too much, actually. Some six months earlier I had seriously considered handing in my notice, bidding a cheery goodbye to untalented poseurs like Dr Ingratiate and all of the professors, decent or otherwise, whose status he coveted so painfully. I would take my chance outside. It had proved quite a bit too soon to make such a move, but the longing to make the break was stronger than ever and I was fully confident it would not be long delayed. I already had stored away, as a treasured aspiration, the moment in the future when I would be able to send in my resignation letter.

Meanwhile, the glorious individualism offered by universities, so often abused and misunderstood but always for me inspirational, provided an enviable refuge. Here I could fulfill my professional obligations, get on with my own writing and research, and ignore everything that I found distasteful. I was also beginning, though dimly as yet, to understand how I could derive certain personal advantages from my new understanding. The more distanced I became, the more I consciously held back from my deluded rivals, the more eager they were to score over me in entirely ineffective ways. I could knowingly leave them free to play a pointless one-sided game. Imperviousness rendered them helpless.

I looked out for Dr Ingratiate and prepared to abase myself before him.

'Who's Monica's Philip?' I asked.

He was delighted, thrilled with my ignorance.

'Gosh, don't you know? You really don't. I thought everyone knew that.'

His pleasure was so intense that he even managed to delay his answer, which he was longing to give, in order to relish this moment of superiority.

'You're serious? You really don't know?'

I assured him that I *was* serious, that I really did *not* know.

'Larkin,' he proclaimed, in a voice suitably simple for someone who, he was thrilled to discover, had just ceased to be a rival and become a harmless child. 'Lar-kin! Larkin *the* Poet. Philip L-a-r-k-i-n.'

I thanked him and went on my way.

The information was not exactly enlightening. I knew who Larkin *the Poet* was, or rather I knew there was a Larkin who was a poet, but not much more than that.

To me he was primarily the author of what at the time I had thought a rather tedious novel called *Jill* which I once been obliged to read as part of the angry young man section of a course on post-war British fiction. I also knew him as the author of the very far from tedious poem 'Church Going' which I had come across in the 1962 revised edition of Kenneth Allott's *Penguin Book of Contemporary Verse*. If I also read at this time Allott's high praise of Larkin in his introductory note to that poem it had not led me to more of the poetry. Much the same must have applied to the once notorious denunciation by A.A. Alvarez in another Penguin anthology *The New Poetry* (1962) of Larkin as a characteristic, unsatisfactory representative of the modern English poetic spirit. There is still a copy of it on my bookshelves which I appear to have bought in 1967. I must have read Alvarez's introduction then, and no doubt some of the poems. If I had been sufficiently interested to turn from these anthologies to Larkin's own individual volumes of poetry, I might even have noticed that the second of them, *The Less Deceived* (1955), was dedicated to Monica Jones.

No doubt this ignorance of mine will be hard for outsiders to credit, though easy, I'm sure, for insiders to understand. The voice of protest sounds perfectly reasonable. 'Are you really asking us to believe Dr Keating that it was possible for a university lecturer in English literature, enthusiastically starting a career at the close of the 1960s, not to be aware of one of the most distinguished, admired, and controversial, living English poets?' The answer I'm obliged to give is 'Yes, very possible indeed.'

Quite apart from there being little justification for the outsider's faith in the omniscience of university English teachers, especially tyros, whose general ignorance, except for a relatively small segment of their subject, is necessarily vast and growing vaster all the time, there's the rarely considered matter of teaching workloads. During the first few years of university teaching, the amount of time spent on simply keeping up with essential reading is so great that I am now convinced that it's a main reason why so many academics give up on the scholarly or writing ambitions they had had as postgraduates. It's here, right at the beginning, that the decay sets in. Research and personal writing are both postponed for a while in order to meet urgent teaching deadlines, and then postponed again, and again.

The pressure truly is that intense. For my first couple of years at Leicester there was barely a moment in any day of the week when I wasn't writing a lecture or seminar talk, preparing a tutorial topic, and marking essays and exams for either the department or the Victorian Studies Centre. Only a tiny proportion of this had anything to do with specialist knowledge I already possessed or was still trying to develop. Many of the authors I was 'teaching' in lectures or tutorials I had barely if ever read before, and whole periods of English literature needed to be plotted or mapped if I was to understand anything of the wider picture. It is probably also at this time when the young tutors, driven to keep up with their students' reading week by week, day by day, begin to develop the academic vices of pronouncing definitively on work they know very little about, and of advancing as authoritative critical judgments that have been rapidly mugged up at second hand. It's all too easy for these survival techniques to become habitual.

In such circumstances, my being hardly aware of Philip Larkin's name was due entirely to practical considerations. If I had had a tutorial coming up on Larkin's poetry, then I would have made it my urgent business to read him, but even so only enough to get by. There wouldn't have been time for any more. Nor did the understanding that Monica was intimately connected with Larkin lead me to seek further knowledge immediately. That would have to wait until I was inspired to get to know and admire the poetry. It was, though, the point from which everything else here takes off.

I left Leicester in the summer of 1972, and never met Monica or spoke to her again. There was no reason why we should have continued to keep in touch. I'm a compulsive non-maintainer of friendships. Monica may well have been the same, and anyway, once our irregular meetings over coffee ceased, the main point of contact between us was gone. Even so, there was one occasion when I should have been in touch with her. My edition of *Cranford* was published in 1976. I didn't forget my inner memo to send a copy to Monica, I just let it drop. I'm sure it's something that many people who have moved from one job to another and quickly lost contact with former colleagues have experienced. 'Why get back in touch now?' I probably asked myself. 'She'll have forgotten all about it.' Such excuses come easily. And after all, I hadn't actually mentioned my intention to her. She wouldn't be expecting a copy to arrive through the post. And if I did send it, then...what? This kind of rationalization is a familiar process, and not sending Monica a copy of *Cranford* can no doubt be placed fairly low among the errors and omissions of my life. It has not been important enough to force me awake in the middle of the night or anything like that. But, for some years it was something I wished I had done.

I only ever saw her once again, and I can't fix that occasion with any confidence. It would now be possible for me to track down the exact date if I wanted to, because from this point in my story the public record is readily available to corroborate such details. But for the moment I shall continue to use it sparingly.

Philip Larkin died in December 1985, so my last sight of Monica would have been shortly after that. It was on a commemorative television programme of the kind that in those days the BBC still felt it a national duty to give to recently dead literary and artistic figures of note. Monica had somehow been persuaded to take part in this particular programme and her contributions to it were blunt and to the point. She leaned forward, glared into the camera, and informed the viewers what an unbelievably self-centred and selfish person Larkin had been. She looked as if she had managed to avoid the make-up people on the way to the screen, but it's more likely that transforming her into a condition of respectability was beyond their skills. Her startling colours were all gone. The uncontrollable hair jutted crazily all over her head. Her face was old, deeply creased and witch-like, her voice bitter and angry. If a caption on the screen hadn't given her name I would never have known who she was. Even after I had absorbed the information that it was her and she reappeared a couple of times I didn't recognize her.

* * * *

When I first met Monica she had seemed to me an academic oddity, a waif or orphan, incomplete or at least uncompleted, someone who, for whatever reason, the university community had failed to assimilate. This view of her was modified slightly as I came to appreciate that for me as well the system just wouldn't do unless I could find some way of holding it permanently at bay. I too was quickly turning into an academic orphan, an oddity. For a while I was inclined to assume that whatever clandestine deals Monica and I had made with our own entirely different selves had been responsible for the friendly nature of the fleeting contacts between us. Now I see that I was not only wrong on this, but doubly so. First, in thinking of Monica's outcast condition as special to her, and wrong again in allowing myself a similar kind of status to hers as an internal exile.

In fact, while our inner stories were unlike each other's, they were not fundamentally different from those of a very large number of other university English teachers. I've no way of knowing whether all academics, whatever their subjects, are much the same, or whether it is only teachers of this particular subject who are the chronic discontents I found so many of them to be. There are certainly good reasons for regarding them as a special case, and also for thinking that the causes of their disease are ingrained, generated by the subject itself.

From the start fears had been expressed that English wasn't a fit and proper subject for academic study. The founding fathers had fought against that prejudice and their dedicated efforts to bring respectability to it were brilliantly successful, for a while at least. The upstart subject was absorbed into universities and the early doubts that it wasn't truly capable of ever becoming a proper academic discipline were largely forgotten. And why not? After all, the ambitions of the best university teachers of English, the dedicated scholarly few who justify the whole extravagant higher educational system, are much the same as those who work in more obviously applied subjects: physics, say, or law or geography or medicine. The justification for the contractual obligations placed on all academics to carry out original research and publish the results of their findings is that their research projects will serve to deepen understanding of their subjects and lead to material or intellectual advances that are taken up by the world outside Academia. That, in the final instance, is why these institutionally privileged lives exist.

Viewed from such an angle all university subjects are applied. To give some arbitrarily chosen examples from the diverse academic research on the go at any one time, new knowledge is sought to help cure terrible diseases; bring a new understanding of the politics, poetry, class structure or whatever of Elizabethan England or eighteenth-century France or twelfth-century Florence; clarify the legal ambiguities underlying society's regulation of crime and punishment; try to reach an understanding of seemingly intractable problems of poverty, wickedness, or child abuse in wealthy societies; keep alive remembrance of past cultures that would otherwise be likely to slip entirely from the memory; discover ways to stop the rivers of the world from becoming sterile; or to preserve the correspondence of great writers and create reliable texts of their work.

It's a noble theory, and of considerable value to society, but unfortunately teachers of English have difficulty in applying it because they are unable to separate their personal selves from their subject. Generally there is a reasonably clear distinction for most university teachers between what they are and what they do, but not for English teachers. They yearn to be what they are teaching, and understandably so. It is, after all, their own language they are studying, the books of their own countrymen they are reading and talking about all the time. They are not doing anything that plenty of other people with or without any specialist training couldn't do just as well. If they were given the chance to be metamorphosed overnight in the manner of Kafka's Gregor Samsa they would happily seize the opportunity, but be transformed not into a grotesque verminous insect but into their very own novel, lyric poem or play.

These incipient masterpieces exist in plenty, shut safely away in offices and studies, often resting uneasily beside an abandoned academic thesis or manuscript. There may not be much of the novel or poem or play down on paper at the moment, and it is absolutely the case that notably few university teachers of English ever do make the essential transition, or indeed any kind of transition as far as writing's concerned, but it's always there as a possibility. Forced to make a choice, there's no doubt which of those two manuscripts they would rush to save if both were threatened in some way. The uncompleted thesis is their attempt to talk about literature: the uncompleted poem or novel *is* literature.

The status of internal exiles that in my academic salad days I mistakenly allotted to Monica and myself was a failure on my part to recognize a condition that was all around us. It wasn't anything special at all. Most of us were infected with a self-destructive discontent, not positively wanting to be where we were or what we were, and incapable of acting decisively to resolve the dilemma. My dreams and literary ambitions were as mundane and predictable as everyone else's. If mine carried any specialness it was in the firmness of my determination to be an active writer, to search out the words and form that would give shape to the kind of literary history that fascinated me. I also trusted that other kinds of writing would develop out of this. I too yearned to be my very own novel, lyric poem, or play. In my case, reaction against what I found at Leicester increased my determination that for me writing must be a continuous activity, never something that could be allowed to trail casually behind me year after year, picked up now and then on the odd weekend or during the vacation, quickly losing any substance it might once have possessed, withering slowly and becoming bitterly resented as yesterday's faded dreams.

Monica conformed with none of this. Her refusal to undertake academic research of any kind except individually through her voracious reading, together with her extension of this self-denying ban to all kinds of writing, placed her in a very special kind of isolation. Nor did any of the alternative options I've suggested apply to her. There was no sign that she wanted to be transformed into a work of literature.

Her immersion in books was not an indication that she was eminently fitted for scholarship. There was no haunting of libraries in order that she might eventually add something of her own to the knowledge they already contained in such abundance. Nor would she have been satisfied to take up the lesser options open to her and settle for becoming a literary pundit or university administrator. All she wanted was to be left alone to fulfil the terms of her university contract as she chose to interpret them. That and nothing else, as far as I could see.

If, as a result of her rejection of everything about her, she had shown an inner contentedness (radiant preferably but merely satisfied would have done) then it might have been possible to believe she had won through to an enviably fulfilled life, even if she was unwilling to reveal the winning formula to anyone else. But she was far from contented. If anything she was more divided than the rest us, more frustrated, more tormented by her academic subject, and more mysteriously so as well. That she could be good company, both funny and irreverent, was never enough to conceal a desperate emptiness beneath the painted face, flamboyant clothes, aimless flirtation, and jaunty posturing. For all her fidgeting and fussing, she was essentially static. During the time I knew her, my first impression of an extravagantly painted Guy Fawkes dummy was never substantially challenged. Everything about her stayed where it was, fixed within her own orbit, never moving out or beyond, never making contact with anything observably present.

But it did all have a point, a meaning, an explanation. For reasons not of my own choosing, and in ways that I had no need to seek out or develop, it was to prove impossible, as I have already said, for me to forget Monica. The private life she concealed with such determination, allowing nothing of it to penetrate our early morning coffee and casual chat, has over the years started to be opened up and made aggressively public. From nothing being known of her private life, there will eventually be made available more information than, it seems reasonable to suppose, most people would ever want revealed about themselves. And although in the process she has not become a work of literature exactly, she is permanently associated with literature of a most remarkable and original kind. Did she know that this was what she was doing? Oh yes. I'm pretty sure she did. At least, I am now. At the time I had no idea of what was going on.

* * * *

When I speculated in my fanciful way that Monica was a creature of the night held in thrall by some dark vampiric force, I was not entirely wrong. She was in thrall all right, only her controlling demon was not Dracula, but Philip Larkin. In a fiercely divided life, her campus days were blank aimless spaces needing to be somehow filled. It was her evenings and nights, woefully empty as I used to imagine them, which actively absorbed her. With the fading away of daylight, her quota of lectures and tutorials met, and the university left thankfully behind her, she returned to a flat that was always imbued with Larkin's spirit, though far less frequently with his physical presence. For most of the time, she had to make do with the spirit alone. Once the front door of the flat was shut behind her, Monica dedicated herself to communicating with Larkin, staying in touch, keeping his interest aroused, not allowing him to stray too far away from her, and planning how regular meetings between them could be managed and maintained.

They had met in 1947 when he took up a post in Leicester university library. At the time Monica was living in a rented flat. Larkin also rented a flat, but only for a short while. On the death of his father in 1948, Larkin's mother wanted to move to Leicester to be near her son. Larkin made the arrangements for her to purchase a house of her own and they lived in it together for the next two years. This arrangement came to a close when Larkin moved away from Leicester in 1950, initially to Belfast for five years, and then permanently to Hull. His mother, who wanted to go to Belfast with him, was persuaded instead to sell the Leicester house and buy a new one in Loughborough where she could live close to her daughter Kitty, Larkin's sister. From this moment, Larkin's own home base became the focal point of a topographical axis that dictated the nature of his relationship with Monica.

While in Belfast, Larkin's travel arrangements were temporary, and necessarily treated as such. But once settled permanently in Hull a clear operational topography was established. It covered a substantial stretch of the Midlands and the north east of England, with Hull (in east Yorkshire) being linked with Loughborough (in north Leicestershire, the homes of Larkin's mother and Kitty), the city of Leicester (Monica's home during term-time), and Haydon Bridge (Monica's vacation retreat in relatively distant Northumberland). A main element in Larkin's popular image is of someone who was static for much of the time, reluctant to emerge from his rented accommodation in Hull. It's true enough that he had no interest in travelling abroad, but his life was anything but static. For year after year, barely a few weeks passed without him travelling backwards and forwards between the Midlands and the North of England. In addition, he would spend regular holidays with his mother or Monica in various parts of England or Scotland. For a long time all of his journeys were by train and only later by car.

When he moved from Belfast to Hull, Larkin had promised his mother he would visit her in Loughborough once a month, and this promise he always kept. When she was ill or under stress he would make the journey more frequently. At these times he would often also visit Monica in Leicester. Christmas he spent in Loughborough with his mother and Kitty's family, again adding in a visit to Monica if she was in Leicester. If she was visiting her own parents for Christmas, she and Larkin would arrange a short holiday break together at a hotel. When staying with Monica at Haydon Bridge he would occasionally travel from there to Loughborough. Far less frequently, Monica would visit Larkin in Hull. The many holidays they took together during university vacations were planned along the same routes, departing from or returning to Haydon Bridge or Hull or Leicester, and including Loughborough on the way.

In addition to the difficulty of keeping this network open, there were other problems to overcome. From the post-war years until deep into the 'permissive' Sixties, repressive sexual attitudes in Britain usually meant that Monica and Larkin could share whatever time they liked with each other as long as they were not seen to be actually sleeping together. And this could apply to the homes of relatives, their own flats, and often hotels as well. In the early days they surrendered to the demands of public respectability. When Monica visited Larkin in Hull she would stay not in his flat but in a nearby hotel. On his visits to Monica in Leicester he would stay with his mother in Loughborough: Monica, though, would never have stayed there with him. On their early holidays together they booked into the same hotel but took separate rooms. More conveniently, they would sometimes rent a holiday home rather than risk a hotel at all. These frustrations only eased as attitudes in Britain began to loosen under the reformist challenges of the Sixties.

Here was the moment, hackneyed though the phrase has become but obviously unavoidable in this context, when 'sexual intercourse began.' There was never a problem about them staying together in Haydon Bridge. Monica would have been strong-minded enough to face down any difficulties that might arise there, though Larkin, characteristically, was bothered by the lustful thoughts and possible approaches this might encourage in local men when Monica was there alone. Still, things between them did now become easier, at least in a logistical sense. They could now book into hotels as a couple, and Monica was regularly staying over in Larkin's flat, and later his house, in Hull.

No wonder she refused to give up one moment of her vacations and followed a work-to-rule policy for the rest of the year. Everything that happened on the Leicester campus was irrelevant compared with her need to keep personal contact with Larkin. The elaborate timetabling was kept largely to herself not because the relationship with Larkin was a secret but because the nature of the relationship meant it could not be managed in any other way. Or rather, in a way that would have been acceptable to Larkin. If it had been a straightforward matter of agreement between them, making the best of a necessarily difficult situation so that they could keep together, then things would have been relatively easy to accept. But they weren't, and never were. For much of the time Monica's position in these arrangements was worryingly precarious. She needed to be constantly alert to any actual or potential breakdowns in their timetables, ready to adjust to itineraries that were laid down by Larkin from motives that were pretty well always his rather than hers.

Larkin's willingness to endure so many cumbersome train journeys, was not primarily due to filial love or duty or to demands imposed upon him by his professional career as a librarian. He was terrified that if he did not keep in regular touch with his mother she might insist on coming to live with him in Hull rather than with Kitty in Loughborough. Similarly, he would often incorporate into his journeys a visit to Monica because he was just as terrified she might insist that the whole fussy business would be easily solved if they got married. Whatever the travel difficulties involved in keeping in touch with the two most important women in his life – and this they most certainly were – Larkin was determined to preserve, on something like his own terms, the solitary life that meant so much to him as both a man and a poet. This could be achieved only as long as his mother remained safely under Kitty's caring eye in Loughborough and Monica remained safely, and relatively independent, in her own flat in Leicester. Trudging backwards and forwards through the Midlands and the North of England was no trouble at all compared with the possible alternatives.

This aspect of Larkin's life had nothing to do with any kind of rambling bohemian freedom. That was a dream that he himself knew he was incapable of turning into reality. The life Larkin yearned for was essentially home based. It provided the subject of some the best of his poems, as also did the unattainable dream of bohemian recklessness. Home for Larkin, though, carried few of its usual domestic connotations. It was a personal space, somewhere occupied by him and no one else, a sanctuary where the poems could develop freely at whatever pace their incubation and maturation demanded without fear of being stifled by the everyday intrusions of other people.

He always preferred to rent rather than own his home because this enabled him to avoid responsibility for looking after the property. Again, any personal discomfort it caused him was regarded as worthwhile. His endless timetabling might have been made easier to manage by telephone, but in those days Larkin's preference for temporary accommodation would have largely ruled that out as a viable option. And anyway, it is difficult to imagine him wanting to have a telephone line installed: it would have placed him at the mercy of the very people he went to so much trouble to keep at a distance. Rigidly excluded from his image of the perfect home were all parental and marital elements. As he wouldn't consider living in any other way, Monica was driven to adjust her own attitudes and live by similar rules. Or rather, she was forced to do so if she wanted to stay with Larkin.

The kind of married-yet-not married relationship they led, though not unknown at the time, was considerably less common then than it has become since. Even so, the relationship between Monica and Larkin had its own tone. Determined by circumstances that Larkin, though not Monica, saw as unchangeable, it was not in any sense a planned agreement, nothing to do with enabling both of them to retain their individual independence. Nor was it about sexual or intellectual equality. This kind of mutuality, so self-consciously prominent a few years later on, was never involved. Instead, they built a relationship that could embrace many of the features of regular domestic married life while excluding the accompanying pressures of daily physical and domestic contact.

It was really only during vacations that they could spend time together as a couple. Otherwise they led separate lives that were focused all but exclusively on the evenings and nights. Daytime was out because unlike most married households at the time, both of them had full-time jobs and they came together only when work was over. Monica, the burden of university temporarily shed, would thankfully abandon the Leicester campus and return to her flat. Larkin's attitude here was similar to Monica's, though his daily routine, containing more and different kinds of business and social commitments, was far more difficult to shrug off. For both there would have been an overwhelming sense of liberation at excluding the outside world. No doubt one of the first evening experiences they celebrated, together though physically apart, would have been to pour their solitary glasses and drink a toast to the coming hours that would see them, in part at least, united.

Some of these moments were given to activities which were no different from those being enjoyed over tea or supper or an evening drink by married couples everywhere in Britain. The radio featured strongly in their plans, and, some years later, television. They listened to *The Archers* with sufficient attention to be able to discuss knowledgeably with each other plot and character developments. This was a fairly regular arrangement. Other radio programmes demanded more careful treatment. When a concert of classical music was announced that was felt by one or other of them to be particularly special they would listen to it at the same time. This meant planning their respective evenings so they could settle down and enjoy the whole thing together from introduction to final applause. For them it became the treasured equivalent of a night out. The same was true of the recordings of live boxing matches that Larkin particularly enjoyed and regular radio programmes about jazz.

Radio was also able to offer them moments of an even more personal nature. As Larkin's reputation grew, his poems were occasionally transmitted on the radio. Sometimes they were read by others, sometimes by himself. If the programme was pre-recorded, then Monica and Larkin could arrange to listen to it together: if live, Monica would follow it avidly, intimately, on her own.

Nor did these simulations of married life exclude the physical. They may not have been together, but there were ways to get round that problem, as there were about arranging a night out in a concert hall with both of them sitting in their respective homes. Larkin was never secretive about his liking for girlie magazines and soft-core photographs and films, or about the accompanying masturbation that enhanced the visual stimulation. In his case, these activities weren't necessarily unavoidable substitutes, forced upon him because there was no living alternative available or possible. For much of the time he preferred them to the real thing. They were less trouble, cheaper, and controlled entirely by himself. Nor did they prevent him from conducting his long-distance intimate relationship with Monica or from having affairs with other women. With careful management, and in these circumstances Larkin was a master of logistics, he ensured that everything could be enjoyed with an absolute minimum of encroachment on his own, very special kind of home-based life.

Monica knew about Larkin's sexual habits and for much of the time she went along actively with them. What she couldn't bear was the thought of a physical rival, another woman who might just snatch from her the marriage prize she always believed might one day be awarded to her. Paper or celluloid women she could cope with. She even aspired to defeat them on their own terms. When together with Larkin, she displayed just for him the kind of lingerie that was standard in the pin-up photos he enjoyed: black knickers and bras, suspender belts, open-net stockings. She not only reserved a collection of sexy underwear for their times together, but wrote to him about it, asking his colour preferences, keeping him informed of her purchases, sexually arousing him from a distance, encouraging him to masturbate to her image rather than that of a professional model. When she achieved this aim, Larkin was perfectly happy to let her know how successful she had been. It was just one of their solitary yet shared experiences. Monica also sent him photographs of herself dressed in items of underwear she knew he particularly liked. It seems probable she used a Polaroid camera, but it's not impossible that she was taught by Larkin to use slightly more sophisticated photographic equipment. After all, he was an accomplished photographer. Some of the familiar photographs of him, known to his many readers from books and newspapers, he had taken of himself using a delayed action device.

The camera was a valuable toy in their sex games, an adjunct to girlie magazines. So were the arousing words in their letters to each other, a literary rather than a visual stimulant. It was all very self-conscious and, one can reasonably assume, potentially without limits. With Monica, Larkin had no need to keep his sexual fantasies to himself. The holiday game they liked to play, sitting together, steadily defacing an Iris Murdoch novel by giving exaggerated sexual meanings to perfectly innocent sentences, is so adolescent, so disturbed as well as disturbing, that it suggests anything was acceptable between them. Whether or not Monica was similarly driven or was manufacturing fantasies for her lover's satisfaction, she was complicit in them.

The games, the titillation and the teasing were for both of them an essential part of their evenings, but it was not, as far as Monica was concerned, the principal element. Nor perhaps for Larkin either. This was, after all, pre-eminently a literary relationship. Once settled into her flat of an evening, Monica's thoughts were set on writing to Larkin. For him too, a letter to Monica was a regular if slightly less frequent part of his evening routine. But for Monica it was essential, unmissable. The university lecturer who was capable of announcing haughtily to anyone who might be interested that she would never put a professional pen to paper, gave herself over every evening, to writing tens of thousands of letters, cards, and notes to Larkin. Millions of words. And he, in response and on his own initiative, wrote constantly to her.

The letters chronicled the small events of their daily lives. Here are details of what they were going to cook for supper; the clothes they had just washed and ironed; what they had enjoyed or not for lunch in their respective university canteens or dining rooms; timings for radio programmes to be listened to; sardonic comments on their university colleagues; arrangements for the next holiday together; their current reading, shared love of animals and their intense hatred of any kind of animal cruelty or suffering. And also, the sexually charged exchanges, the tender expressions of how much they truly meant to each other: the cards, presents, and pet names. As a constant, edgy theme, there were the discussions of marriage, advanced tentatively by a Monica determined never to sound pushy or demanding and met by lengthy diversionary tactics from Larkin. Frequently apparent was the guilt he willingly suffered from knowing exactly what it was that Monica wanted, his open acknowledgement of the reasonableness of her demands upon him, and his carefully considered refusals to do anything about them.

As the years passed, Larkin's growing fame as a poet, coupled with heavy official duties as a university librarian, imposed new strains on their relationship. He was obliged to deal with an ever increasing number of public engagements or semi-official duties, either as poet or librarian. When these duties were based in Hull, with Monica not included, Larkin would go alone or take another woman and either keep the information from Monica or assure her that it was an entirely innocent arrangement, which it might or might not have been. On many of the larger London-based public engagements Monica was increasingly included as the official consort she regarded herself as being. And, appearing to deny her right to any such position, there were all the things not said, not proffered for sharing, notably Larkin's extraordinary deviousness in concealing his intricate affairs with other women, his playing off of one against the other, admitting one moment that he was involved with someone else and half-denying it the next. For Larkin, all the shifting and sliding was directed at maintaining the only position that truly mattered to him. His beleaguered home he protected like an ancient citadel, building inner wall after inner wall, forcing any potential invader to overcome one daunting obstacle after another to get at him.

Monica did finally break through the outer defences, though only in a way that was not truly welcomed by either of them. On the point of taking early retirement from Leicester, she suffered a series of accidents and illnesses. There was only Larkin to turn to for help, and he had no alternative but to invite Monica to join him in Hull. They agreed it would be only until she recovered, but it quickly became permanent. If Monica was no longer able to look after herself, Larkin himself was hardly in better shape to take command. As well as both of them being chronically ill, they were also drunk for much of the time and able only to rustle up rudimentary meals. If Larkin hadn't finally surrendered and taken Monica in, the letters between them would no doubt have continued to be written somehow. It was a compulsion that Monica especially would have been unable to control, illness or not. But now, physically together in a parody of the married life she had always longed for, there was no need for the letters and they stopped.

Although it was Monica's illness that finally brought them together under the same roof, it was Larkin who died first. After his death in 1985, Monica lived on for a further sixteen years in the only house Larkin had ever owned, a house that was now hers. After their brief spell together, she was once more alone, this time entirely without him. There was not even the long-distance consolation that the exchange of letters had once provided, though some kind of consolation was needed more than ever. Larkin's posthumous fame was established with astonishing ease as a biographer (Andrew Motion) and editor (Anthony Thwaite), both of whom were respected poets and had been known personally to Larkin, set speedily to work on the life, poems and letters. Even the emergence from all of this of a very unpleasant politically incorrect side to Larkin's character failed to do anything other than create a temporary halt in the consolidation of his reputation. In no time at all he was widely accepted not only as the major English poet of the second half of the twentieth century, but also the most admired and popular. It was all achieved with a promptitude and efficiency rare in literary history.

For Monica there was no time to back away, pause, or hug to herself the part she had played in Larkin's story. As one of Larkin's executors, and someone with an unrivalled private knowledge of Larkin, she became, willingly or not, a participant in the biographical and editorial work, and this meant her being exposed to areas of his life she had previously known nothing about, or at best had dimly, painfully suspected. She was obliged to confront evidence that other women had also possessed private knowledge of Larkin's life, experiences which were in certain respects not all that different from hers: some of them were even at times distressingly similar. Before she died, hidden away from the world yet caught up unavoidably in the rapid publication of Larkin's life and letters, she would have been obliged to relive the vast correspondence she had shared with Larkin over some forty years.

Here was her Philip, the treasured memories both warm and sad, but also a side of him she would no doubt have preferred not to have had placed so vividly before her. In print for everyone to identify were the lies and deviousness, the half-truths and avoidances, presented with all of Larkin's formidable literary skills, that only Monica would ever be able fully to interpret. The message their correspondence now conveyed to her must have been that, whatever Larkin's true feelings for her, he had never wished or intended that one day they would be truly united. She might even have come to learn that if he ever had genuinely cherished such feelings about any woman, it probably wouldn't have been her. The life Monica had actually lived with Larkin was all he ever intended it to be, that and nothing more, no matter what she might have hoped it might one day become. This was the bitter message she would have nursed in her final years of drunken solitude in Hull, the half-crazed disillusionment of the woman I had seen but not recognized on television shortly after Larkin's death.

* * * *

It's impossible for me to exaggerate how little I knew about any of these events or the two people involved in them, back in Leicester all those years ago. Even after Dr Ingratiate-desperate-for-a-Chair had unwittingly provided me with the necessary key my ignorance remained pretty well total. It was still some years before I really began to read Larkin's poetry for myself, and still more years before I came to value him as a 'writer,' the word rather than 'poet' that Monica decided to have placed on his gravestone. The justness of that distinction I came to appreciate only when I discovered his remarkable prose, especially his writings on jazz.

At Leicester, I had no idea of the extent of Larkin's interest in jazz, let alone the controversial nature of his views. Nor was I aware that he was then just about to give up writing the jazz record reviews he had contributed to the *Daily Telegraph* for the previous decade. This particular ignorance of mine is all the more striking because my experiences of jazz were in certain respects remarkably similar to his, something that Monica had grasped immediately. How uninformed was it possible for me to be? Well, setting jazz aside for one moment, I was also totally unaware that in this same period Larkin was awarded an honorary degree by Leicester University. It would have been sponsored presumably by either the department of which I was a member or the university library that I frequented every day. I still can't quite believe this happened, but according to his biographer Andrew Motion, it did. My distaste for the everyday realities of academic life and my eagerness to distance myself from them had obviously developed even faster and deeper than I realized.

Looking back, prompted by my growing appreciation of Larkin's poetry and aided by the ever expanding public record of his life, it often feels that my scant memories of Monica have survived in me as a kind of secret code that over the years has demanded constant reinterpretation, slowly, gradually, a bit at a time. Whatever truth has emerged needs to be largely conjectural rather than definitive, a clarification of images that could only come into focus retrospectively. It now seems clear, for example, that Monica was not simply living a divided life in Leicester. She was doing that all right, but she was also creating a mysterious daytime persona that was very largely a reflection, even at times a recreation, of her night-time experiences. The spirit of independence she flaunted was similarly divided. Simply to maintain her relationship with Larkin in the way she did over such a long period of time is evidence enough that her inner life was pretty well everything to her. The defiant show she put on of not caring what anyone thought about her was no empty posture, but any independence she attained still rested on her giving herself totally to Larkin. Whatever her inner triumphs, outwardly she came over as a woman possessed. Apart perhaps from the eclectic reading she had brought into the relationship with Larkin, everything else owed its existence to his influence, even her pervasive melancholy.

The possibility that I might have listened to the same boxing match or the same jazz records that he and she had enjoyed together turned me into a welcome harmless surrogate, allowing her to prolong her evening's pleasure into daylight. Neither I nor anyone else in a similar position to me, would have had any idea of what she was up to. She must have been constantly re-enacting scenes like these.

For much of the time her conscious mind would have been elsewhere, with the daytime protective screen she created for herself shielding far more than the opinions and attitudes she did voice. The flamboyant gestures and poses with which she would decorate our conversations might well have been similar to those she had been using more effectively just a few hours earlier with Larkin, in letters or photographs or in later years on the telephone. The repeat performances, though, were asexual. Now that the more erotic aspects of those hidden Leicester evenings have become known it is even tempting to take a larger view of Monica's personality and regard her idiosyncratic everyday dress as a defiant public display of the kind of thing that her man liked so much in private. And if that message wasn't intended to be understood by those around her, the accompanying stance of not caring what anyone else thought of her, certainly was. After all, these props and ploys were not being used by her to try to attract men. That was what was so strange about them. What purpose could they have represented other than a determined effort to assert that there was, actually, quite a bit more to her than those around her imagined? As an additional defiant taunt, she might have been adding: 'Not that you're ever going to learn anything about it from me.' Even then she couldn't resist playing with the material of her secret life, rerunning it for her own daytime satisfaction whenever the chance arose.

The jazz enthusiasms and attitudes that Monica expressed to me can all be found, where I myself was surprised to find them many years later, in Larkin's own collection of his jazz record reviews *All What Jazz* (1970; revised ed., 1985). This book was joined, posthumously, by *Reference Back* (1999) a gathering of Larkin's jazz book reviews and miscellaneous articles edited by Richard Palmer and John White that was later reissued as *Larkin's Jazz* (2001). All of these writings on jazz are deeply personal to Larkin, their distinctive tone and manner being closely related to the poetry. That the rare quality they possess has not been more widely recognized is easily explained. *Reference Back* was edited by two of the relatively few people around at the time who were sufficiently informed on jazz to appreciate just how much it all meant to Larkin. By then it was already clear that an intimate knowledge of jazz could not be taken for granted even in Larkin's semi-official biographers and editors, while to a still younger generation of Larkin commentators it can not be generally assumed to exist at all.

Larkin himself anticipated this possibility. He knew that while the emotional range of his poetry was capable of appealing to readers of different ages and types, present and future, his passion for traditional jazz would survive only as a niche interest. It was perhaps for the same reason that he didn't even try to introduce the distinctive rhythms, language, and forms of jazz into his poetry. In his celebrated introduction to *All What Jazz* he allowed that the music he so admired was the product of a particular moment of social and cultural history, merely one form of expression of what he calls the 'unique private excitement that youth...always seems to demand.' For his generation this happened to be traditional jazz, but in another age it might have been 'drink or drugs, religion or poetry.' Or, he could have said, with more immediate relevance, pop or rock or electronic music or indeed modern jazz, the alternatives that did in fact rapidly displace Larkin's own youthful form of 'private excitement.'

This keen historical sense pervades Larkin's writing on jazz. He set himself the double task of documenting both the nature of the special attraction that jazz had to young people like him in the first half of the twentieth century and also the demise of that attraction. Jazz as he had experienced it was dying and being transformed into something quite different. Already there were fewer people around who felt as he did. Soon they would hardly exist at all. This was why he gave up reviewing. The jazz records that now came to him for assessment were either archival (and loved by him) or contemporary (and disliked). Larkin injected into his writings about jazz a mournful elegiac tone, consciously evoking the final moments of the most original music of the twentieth century.

One of the more melancholy responsibilities that fell to him in the *Daily Telegraph* reviews throughout the Sixties was to commemorate the deaths of great jazz musicians. He took to the task with brutal honesty, evaluating the achievements of individual jazz musicians and allotting them places on his own idiosyncratic musical scale. Their ranking depended largely on whether Larkin believed they had contributed to the joyful life of jazz or its incipient death. His obituary notices of formative jazz figures such as George Lewis, Pee Wee Russell, and Johnny Hodges were admiring and deeply respectful, but his treatment of the arch-modernist John Coltrane was so contemptuous that the *Telegraph* chose not to publish it. Unrepentant, Larkin included the piece unchanged in *All What Jazz*. Monica would have lived through these moments, not only with the *Telegraph* spread before her on the mornings the reviews appeared, but with her sense of what was being said in them augmented by Larkin's raw emotions, whether anger or grief, which he would probably already have communicated to her by letter or phone. As for me, I wasn't even aware of the existence of the reviews. Not that that mattered necessarily. For what Monica carried to our morning coffee from her overnight contacts with Larkin, could sometimes be significantly mingled with, even transfigured by, very different emotional experiences than those that Larkin himself had expressed.

'It's terrible news about Bunny, isn't it? I thought I might have seen you before this. You're the only person here who'd understand. There's no one else to speak to about it.'

As I have said, I *didn't* understand, though I felt I had managed to get myself out of a potentially awkward situation without too much embarrassment. Now I'm not so sure. Johnny Hodges' affectionate, widely known nickname was Rabbit. Larkin himself uses it in his reviews. It was sometimes abbreviated to 'Rab' by Duke Ellington and other personal friends, though as far I can see, Hodges was never called Bunny by anyone. 'Bunny' along with its diminutive 'Bun' was Monica herself, Larkin's long-term loving name for her. Throughout their relationship, rabbits/bunnies were a constant, playful, linguistic reference for them, based partly on their joint admiration for Beatrix Potter and partly on their passionate hatred of any kind of cruelty to animals. Larkin wrote Monica birthday poems and jingles on the theme. In his letters he constantly calls her Bun or Bunny (and sometimes Rabbit), and his published poems about animals such as 'Myxomatosis' carried special significance for both of them.

At the time of Hodges' death and Larkin's brief appreciative obituary in the *Daily Telegraph* Monica was once again suffering deep anxiety over her Hull rival. She was unsure about the true nature of the relationship and what Larkin really felt about it. The uncertainty was a cause of constant pain and worry to her. For years Larkin had characteristically refused to make clear what exactly was going on, but Monica knew that if the affair was serious it could mean the end of her. It was not Rabbit/Hodges whose death was being mourned in Leicester but Bunny/Monica's. Nor was it primarily a wonderful age of jazz that she could see drawing to its inevitable end, but the long tortuous relationship between her and Larkin. No wonder I was puzzled by the depth of feeling she revealed in breaking the news of Bunny's death to me.

The consolation I had hastily offered her that day also involved Larkin, though in a very different way. Let's wait until Louis goes before we pull the curtain, I had suggested, and that seemed to cheer her up: 'Oh yes, that's true enough. It's not all over as long as Satchmo's around.' Unknowingly, I was offering her Larkin's own line on the final closure of the type of jazz he had adored. With Hodges I had trailed unknowingly behind both Larkin's obituary and Monica's awareness of it. With Armstrong I was slightly ahead of them, though soon to be overtaken. Larkin's obituary of Armstrong took much the same line as I would have done, celebrating someone who was to be remembered not just as a great jazz musician but, without qualification, as 'an artist of world stature.'

Here was also an opportunity for Larkin to reinforce his wider conviction that the passing of Armstrong marked the end of true jazz, an event foreshadowed by the earlier deaths of musicians like Hodges and Russell. The Armstrong obituary was almost the last jazz record review that Larkin wrote for the *Telegraph*. He had wanted to give them up three years earlier, but had been persuaded not to. Now with 'the great oak uprooted at last,' as Larkin romantically described Armstrong's passing, it was all over. What was there left for him to review? Or, as Monica, may well have been thinking, what part was left for her? 'You said he'd be the next to go' was how she had misremembered my attempted consolation. Now he had gone. Everything was drawing to a close, everything was under threat, including whatever restricted role Monica might still be able to play in her relationship with Larkin. Would she be the next to go?

All she could hope for was to survive, much as Miss Matty does in *Cranford,* the book that Monica found too sad to contemplate. In true Victorian manner, Miss Matty's inherent goodness, the radiant example she offers to everyone around her, is justification enough for her existence. That at least is the outward message. But the great strength of the book lies in the way Gaskell sees beyond and beneath this sweet stoical surface to the years of inner pain and lack of personal fulfilment. Miss Matty's early hope of marriage to a man she loves is destroyed by her family's fake gentility, leaving the pretty young girl to live and die 'an old maid.' There are the dreams she experiences throughout her life of having a child of her own that, for her, are never to be anything but dreams, and the faded love letters exchanged between her mother and father that she treasures, carefully rereads and then burns, slowly and regretfully because 'no one will care for them when I am gone.' And always, however old she becomes, the persistent feeling that marriage can never be regarded as entirely impossible: 'Marry!' gasps Miss Matty, astonished along with everyone else at the news that Lady Glenmire has come to an 'understanding' with Mr Hoggins. 'Well! I never thought of it. Two people that we know going to be married. It's coming very near!'

I once regretted that I hadn't kept the promise made to myself to send a copy of my edition of *Cranford* to Monica. Now I'm rather glad I didn't send it to her.

Not, of course, that Monica was a Victorian heroine capable of finding compensation for her own unfulfilled life in the assurances of friends and relatives that they all thought she was wonderful. She wouldn't have expected anything like that, and anyway there was no chance of her getting it. Yet if she had wanted to seek compensation, and during those final solitary years in Hull she must have longed constantly to do so, it was to be found everywhere in the poetry of the man she had loved obsessively and placed at the heart of her own intensely focused life.

Virtually all of the poems which have become so famous, and deeply valued by so many people, carry Monica's influence. Not in any grand sense of her having been some kind of hidden collaborator, but simply because she was always devotedly and honestly there, connected with the original experiences of the poems and their subsequent development. Larkin trusted Monica's ear, her knowledge of literature and critical sense. In the early days especially he would send her drafts of his poems to read and criticize, sometimes admitting that he himself didn't really think they were much good. Monica was capable of seeing that very often they were quite a bit more than that and would tell him so. If his uncertainty was justified she wouldn't hesitate to confirm him in that as well. Occasionally, at her suggestion a key word or line was changed: the striking 'losels' instead of Larkin's less original 'lazars' is hers in 'Toads' though direct participation of this kind was relatively unusual. Larkin wasn't, generally, the kind of poet who was driven to seek advice from others. That he sent poems at all to Monica whether asking for her judgment or simply to read, was a sure sign of how much he respected her opinion. From the early tentative 'Wedding-Wind' and 'Spring' and the first popular success 'Church Going,' through to the mature, cockily confident 'Vers de Société' and 'This be the Verse,' she was usually the first reader of a Larkin poem – very often the *only* reader before publication – whether in draft or final state.

While Monica herself was not often the acknowledged subject of a Larkin poem, she did provoke the sexual bleakness of 'Talking in Bed' and was sufficiently aware of the fact to be worried about what Larkin's mother and sister might read into the poem. She is the declared recipient of the playful academic distinctions made in 'Poem about Oxford,' which is also, incidentally, a poem about Leicester and Hull. But whether acknowledged or not, her presence can never be avoided simply because she was very often present, either personally with Larkin or in the letters, and so decisively and influentially so that the extent of whatever contribution she may have made at the time, in conversation or discussion or attitude, can never be fully recovered. Only Monica and Larkin could possibly have known how much or how little it all amounted to.

But to appreciate just a few of the many possibilities, she is the 'friend' travelling in the train with Larkin in 'I Remember, I Remember' who prompts his sour memories of youthful non-events in Coventry and the

153

characteristically glum conclusion: 'Nothing, like something, happens everywhere.' When staying together in Haydon Bridge, they would often visit the Bellingham, a local country show. These outings, hugely enjoyed by Larkin, produced the minute social detail of 'Show Saturday,' his remarkable short story or sketch in verse. Monica was with him in Chichester Cathedral when his attention was caught by 'An Arundel Tomb.' Later he discussed the poem's composition with her stage by stage. In a very different mood, she was standing beside him in front of a defaced poster of a bathing beauty at Tweedmouth, Northumberland (and no doubt advancing some pithy views of her own about it) that he would transform with great effect into 'Sunny Prestatyn.'

She was the recipient of the first draft of 'Days' a 'tiny little poem' that Larkin claimed to consider barely a poem at all. Even so, he sent it to her, carefully drawing her attention to the fact that it marked for him a change of style. When after sixteen frustrating years of effort, he made one last desperate effort to complete 'The Trees,' it was to Monica he sent the draft of the poem asking her whether she felt it all fitted together. The gestation of that poem was unusually long, but it was quite common for references to poems to be spread over a number of years, so intimate and so continuous was the communication between them. Monica was the first person to hear that on the way to visit his mother, Larkin had been fascinated by the many 'importunate wedding parties' he observed crowding the platforms of every station the train passed through on its way to Grantham. Three years later, the puzzle finally and fruitfully resolved, he would consult her about the 'fiendish' difficulty he was having with the final stanza of 'The Whitsun Weddings.'

When, in August 1955, Monica listened to three poems by Larkin being read on the radio, she was struck particularly by 'Mr Bleaney.' She was sufficiently impressed by it to offer Larkin a deeply personal tribute: 'Oh, I am sure that you are the one of this generation! I am sure you will make your name...really be a real poet.' This was no easy flattery, as she herself was quick to explain. Not that she needed to do so. She was already intimate enough with Larkin himself as well as his poetry to be amused at recognizing how like Mr Bleaney he was. 'Your catalogue of the room's shortcomings! Like you & like me – I smiled at the radio as if I were smiling at you as it was read.' So much of their future is captured in that moment. Her lifetime of devotion to both the man and his poetry, of course, but the distance as well as the closeness, the foresight that communication between them would always take place between separate isolated rooms, from, as it were, a Mr Bleaney to an Ms Bleaney. Here that recognition 'like you & like me' could still be expressed light-heartedly. In the future it could just as well be a matter of frustration, worry, anger, pain, isolation.

But the communication itself never stopped: it was barely interrupted. No doubt Larkin would still have become 'a real poet' if he had never met Monica, though we can never know that for sure. What is certain is that he wouldn't have become the same poet, so profoundly was he influenced by the relationship. And not only in the ways that can be easily discerned, but also in a vast number of ways that can now only be guessed at. The travels, holidays, phone calls, letters, sexual play, boxing matches and jazz record request programmes, the constant sheering away from marriage, the lifetime of shuttling between his mother and his lover, were crucial elements in the process by which Larkin did become the very real poet he is. And, in addition to Monica contributing so much in so many different ways to help make this particular poet's life so singular, there were the poems, to be read, discussed, assessed, praised or criticized, helped on their way. All of this was also taking place, unknown to me certainly and probably to most other people as well, in that mysteriously closed-off, earth-strewn flat in Leicester half a century ago.

Trevor

In short, he so buried himself in his books that he spent his nights reading from twilight till daybreak and the days from dawn till dark; and so from little sleep and much reading, his brain dried up and he lost his wits.

Cervantes, *Don Quixote* (1614). Translated by J.M.Cohen

In the early 1980s I was nearing the end of a research project that had preoccupied me for the whole of the previous decade. It was a complicated business, an elaborate web of literary and historical associations, still unfocused but on the way to completion. Once everything was joined up I was hoping to be able to offer a coherent social and economic context for late Victorian and early twentieth-century fiction. That was my intention. That was the project.

The temporary title or short-hand code I used to describe it was 'the emergence of modernism.' I knew this was too cumbersome a title to be carried forward into print and would eventually need to be replaced by something less portentous, but I wanted to stay with it for as long as possible. It expressed my aims too precisely to be abandoned just yet. After all, what concerned me was a process rather than a complete or finished state. I was not interested in trying to define the nature of modern fiction or to assess the principal writers engaged in it. Literary criticism had settled these matters long ago and I was largely in agreement with its conclusions. What interested the historian in me were questions that literary critics didn't usually think worth pursuing. I wanted to know how it had all come about and why modern fiction had taken on its distinctive literary forms and social attitudes.

Scholarly work of this kind is necessarily slow, and although by the early 1980s I had completed much of the basic research as well as something like three-quarters of the writing, I estimated it would be at least another eighteen months or so before I could think of having a manuscript ready to send to the publisher. That was fine by me. Getting the pattern right was the main thing. In comparison, taking another year or two over it was of little importance. For the first time, I was beginning to feel I knew where the individual parts of my research belonged. The pattern, the story, was at last taking some kind of recognizable shape.

Over the years I had become used to working in the dark, barely able at times to see those individual parts let alone grasp the many possible relationships between them. All I could do was leave them to grow, trusting that at some point they would move closer together and discover each other, as it were. Or, if that sounds a bit too mystical, I had now reached a position where I felt able to set aside the fragments until they could be fitted together into a single picture. But, whether natural growth or hard slog deserved the credit for whatever progress had been made, and allowing, in this particular case, that one of them wasn't much good without the other, I was pretty sure that some kind of conclusion was near at hand.

No doubt it is already apparent that I was feeling rather pleased with myself, exhilarated even, though not entirely unworried. The work that remained to be done was largely a matter of strengthening connections, checking back, restructuring. This meant that my mind was now in the fairly comfortable position of revisiting old sites rather than exploring unfamiliar regions. The basic reading was as complete as it ever would be, and that, in itself, was a cause of some satisfaction.

Way back at the start, before the darkness descended, when there was only the vaguest of plans and no pattern at all, the possibility of ever being able to get the necessary reading done seemed the most intractable of my problems, and when an opportunity came to transfer from Leicester to Edinburgh I had gone for it enthusiastically. Other possible advantages and disadvantages of the move apart from the chance of getting myself in a position where I could read prolifically were barely thought about. Everything else was subsumed within that one huge concern.

In those days it was commonly said that moving to Scotland from England meant a disorienting step back in time of about ten years. And, sure enough, that was how it felt. I left Leicester in the early Seventies and arrived in Edinburgh in the early Sixties. I've no idea whether the generalization was applicable to the whole of Scotland, but it fitted the university of its capital city to perfection, and this was an issue I was well fitted to judge. At the University of Sussex where I had been both an undergraduate and a postgraduate the curriculum had actively fostered interdisciplinary studies. These had been further encouraged in a more specialized sense at Leicester where a similar approach was employed in the postgraduate courses run by the Victorian Studies Centre. Moving to Edinburgh meant cutting myself loose from these influential institutions. I was exchanging an academic environment that was actively sympathetic to the work I wanted to do in the immediate future, for an old-fashioned, rigidly departmental system that showed no interest in moving beyond the boundaries of individual disciplines.

It might have been considered a foolish decision for someone intent on building an academic career out of his personal research, but I wasn't. When I moved to Edinburgh I had no wish to spend the rest of my working life in universities and didn't expect to do so. Nor was I committed to a particular theoretical or ideological approach which might have benefited from a specific change of university. In this respect, my principal concern was how to devise a methodology that would enable me to weave my interdisciplinary web. As I regarded this as an entirely personal matter, moving a decade back in time mattered little to me. It was far more important to have a good library on hand. That's not always a problem for academics. Many scholars, whether north or south of the border, have research interests that are monographic, based on specific authors or themes. They are therefore able, in one way or another and without too much trouble, to obtain most of the books they need whether their own university library is large or small. But researchers who are drawn to broad or expansive projects are placed at a serious disadvantage by limited library facilities.

It had not taken much experience of university life for me to come to the rather disturbing understanding with myself that I could manage perfectly well with little support from either institutions or institutional people. But I simply couldn't do without a very good library, or, to be more precise, loads of books. Had it been necessary I would happily have dispensed with the library itself as long as I could get my hands on its essential contents, but, of course, there was no chance of that happening. The books I longed for didn't come by themselves, and a library that was simply well stocked wasn't enough. In fact, not much of an advance on surrounding myself with books of my own, and this I had already done, at home and at the university. No, the library I wanted would need to be bulging at the sides with books, with more of them hidden in miles of subterranean stacks and still more piled in outside warehouses. Ideally, the supply would be endless.

Leicester had been unable to offer anything resembling this formidable ideal. But Edinburgh came close because it housed one of the six British copyright libraries which are entitled to receive free copies of all books published in Britain. This was a national matter, a legislative affair that had grown out of the union between Scotland and England, and had nothing as such to do with Edinburgh university, though it didn't feel like that. For Edinburgh is a relatively small capital city, and the National Library of Scotland was not simply near the university or within easy reach or anything vaguely promising like that. It was just along the road. There would be no more fussing with batches of interlibrary loan forms and xeroxed copies of the real thing; no frustrating delays or long journeys to consult an item that might or might not be of use; no long lists of books to be sought out during the vacations because they were unavailable locally. Of course, not all the books I might need to look at were ever going to be found together in one place. Even a copyright library couldn't promise that. The endless supply *was*, after all, a dream. But a surprisingly large proportion of the material I needed was in the National Library of Scotland, and almost everything else was likely be stored in the British Museum. Regular complementary trips to central London were therefore a necessity, and as at that time there was nowhere else in the world I would rather be, my research trips were a perfect blend of work and pleasure.

And that was how it felt as I headed south very early in January 1981. The date is strictly according to the calendar, for just as nothing much had changed north of the border in the previous decade, so it felt that not much was changing to any great extent elsewhere in Britain either. Disappointingly and unexpectedly so. Eighteen months earlier, an upsurge of electoral enthusiasm had brought the Conservatives back into power. But the palpable sense of hope they carried with them had swiftly faded and Britain seemed once again ready to sink back into its habitual post-war mood of political and social stasis.

So, the date on the new calendars might just as well have read 5 January 1971 when, with the Hogmanay celebrations still barely over, I settled into my train seat at Waverley Station. I was off to London for what I hoped would be one final rummage among the archives of the Authors' Society. The university was due to reopen shortly, but as I had no scheduled classes in the first few days of the new term I could spend something like a whole week at the British Museum. That was long enough for me to revisit all those bitter squabbles between late Victorian publishers and authors, and also, to consider once again the extraordinary willingness of so many people of that time to endure the chaos of an age of transition because of the glorious settled future they were convinced would eventually emerge from it. Once again I would need to confront all those dreams of moving ever forward and upwards, most of them now long since abandoned or exploded, or upended. It was difficult at times for me not to feel like H.G.Wells's time traveller, scrambling on to his adapted bicycle and peddling optimistically into the future (or perhaps the past), arriving in a better (or perhaps worse) world, confronting an age of progress (or perhaps regression).

I was similarly unsure in which direction I was personally heading or whether I should be cheerful or sad at the present omens. The change of government that had so recently promised a new way out of seemingly insoluble social problems, appeared to have turned itself into another stalled transition, another case of uncertainty about where exactly it was pedalling. That was gloomy but not entirely disheartening. At least my research felt as though it was shaping up into a meaningful pattern.

It could hardly be expected to solve any of our current problems, but it might help explain, to my satisfaction if nobody else's, how some of them had come about.

The first days of the new year in Edinburgh had been fresh and bright. No snow, no sleet, no rain, not much wind. It hadn't even been very cold. As the train moved south it became clear that everyone else in Britain must have been enjoying the same unseasonably mild weather. Just before York there were a few showers of snow heavy enough to cover the train windows, but they had disappeared long before I arrived in London. I took the underground to Leicester Square, walked down St Martin's Lane and round the edge of Trafalgar Square to the rambling, decaying Edwardian grandeur of the Commonwealth Society in Northumberland Avenue where I had reserved a room.

By about three o' clock I had unpacked, retraced the greater part of my earlier walk down from King's Cross, and claimed a vacant seat in the British Museum Reading Room. There, I was told that the books I had ordered could not be brought from storage until later that evening. I thought about going straight through to the manuscripts room, but decided instead to make do with the reference books that lined the walls of the Reading Room. The Society of Authors' archive could wait until tomorrow.

I don't know whether it's true that the shape of the Reading Room was designed as a simulation of the human brain, with the layered walls and galleries of books running like veins all around it, reaching up to the edge of the great dome itself and serving as a symbolic representation of the intellectual toil of the scholars seated below. Perhaps few people think about that nowadays because the scholars have all been moved up to St Pancras and plugged into machines. But in those days it was generally regarded as a plausible explanation of the Reading Room's distinctive shape. I was reasonably happy with it, whether true or not, but I did also have an additional theory of my own. It wasn't any kind of replacement or even an alternative theory: more of a slightly irreverent adjunct.

I always felt that with its catalogue carousel at the centre and the encircling rows of desks ranged symmetrically around it, the Reading Room could be regarded not only as a symbol of scholarly effort over the ages but also as a convenient practical aid to some of the less dignified aspects of human communication. If you took a slow walk round the outer edge of the room, it was possible to scrutinize every row of seats there, and, in exchange for four or five minutes worth of your time, learn whether or not anyone you knew was present at that particular moment. It was true that not everyone could be expected to be in their seats at the same time. Some would be outside having a smoke or in one of the smaller reading rooms or the toilets or the restaurant or taking a refreshing walk around Bloomsbury or whatever. Even so, the theory functioned well enough. However restless readers were liable to become during the day, most of them did start out from under the dome, and I've no doubt that every one of them had made, at one time or another, the kind of recce I've described, albeit for very different reasons. Being naturally unsociable, my interest in this kind of quick survey was concerned more with the people I would take care to avoid rather than those I looked forward to meeting up with.

Derek Wisthrop's attitude was quite different from mine. About three years earlier he had published a learned, rather flashy study of twentieth-century party politics in Britain called *Positive Cynicism* which had become something of a bestseller. He taught philosophy at one of the London University colleges in nearby Bloomsbury and was an academic gossip by profession. Whenever he was in the British Museum, which seemed to be most of the time, he would make the circuit of the reading room at fairly regular intervals to be quite sure he missed no one he thought worth cornering. As my interest in the personal goings-on within universities was all but non-existent, I wouldn't have expected to occupy a place on Derek's list, though I obviously qualified for some other reason because my name was there all right and had been for a number of years. He was so assiduous in his tracking operations that a chat together had become a regular feature of my research trips to London. On this bright January afternoon Derek had located me in the Reading Room, talked me out of my seat, and led me across Great Russell Street into a café, all within thirty minutes of my arrival.

'I was hoping I'd see you,' he said, his voice rising dramatically and then falling languidly in order to convey a mingled sense of excitement and boredom. 'Not simply for my own pleasure which is, of course, boundless. I'm a messenger. I've been commissioned to contact you.'

'Commissioned?'

'Asked.'

'To *contact* me?'

'If I knew you.'

Derek's florid manner of speech took some getting used to. It usually needed to be translated before it could be made to yield much sense. I've heard it described as typically Oxford, and that may be the case, though if so it would have to have been an indirect influence because, like me, Derek had hardly ever stepped inside the place. He had been an undergraduate at Manchester before doing postgraduate research in London. There, rapidly and in swift succession, he had obtained a post teaching philosophy, achieved his popular success with *Positive Cynicism*, been promoted to a readership on the strength of that success, and become much in demand on radio programmes as a commentator on politics and the arts. All of this, carefully managed, still left him largely and happily free to haunt the British Museum.

Derek was conscious enough of his own silliness for me to be able to respond to his approaches with mock annoyance.

'What on earth are you talking about?'

'*What* I'm talking about is a man called Trevor Barclay. Have you heard of him?'

'I have not.'

'I thought you might have done. By association, at least. I realize, of course, that you don't actually know each other. Hence my mission. And I should say that *I* hardly know *him*. But it was just possible that you could have known *of* him. He's one of your Eng Lit crowd. Not Victorian though. He's a medievalist, with a special interest in Malory.

Sir Thomas that is. Actually I was interviewing someone recently who claimed that Malory wasn't a knight at all but a Welsh monk. Do you know about that? Anyway, Arthurian literature, that's Trevor's thing. And the knights themselves rather than simply Malory. Lancelot... Galahad...Percival...Gawain?'

Derek paused and glared at me questioningly as though to make sure I was still with him. It was another of his mannerisms. Some kind of self-defence mechanism, I imagine, to the responses he must have got all the time from people irritated at finding themselves unexpectedly under interrogation. I nodded smugly and pulled a long enough face to persuade him that I *was* familiar with the principal occupants of the Round Table. He not only took the wordless hint, but muttered apologetically, 'of course, of course.'

We sat silently for a few moments while Derek prepared himself to get to the point.

'Well,' he said eventually. 'As I say, I don't know much about Trevor. I wouldn't be surprised if no one else does either. He's nice enough, but unforthcoming. Keeps himself very much to himself. Like you, I suppose. Mind you that's about all you do have in common. There's none of your *hauteur* about him. It could be that he's shy. At best, that is. Or lacking in confidence, probably weak. It may simply be that the old ego needs a bit of a boost. It might help if he published something on those wretched medieval soap operas to explain why we should still bother with them.'

He paused to see if his rhetoric was having any effect on me. When I refused him an opening, he said, 'Or, it could have something to do with the place he's at.' Lowering his voice conspiratorially he named a polytechnic situated, as the narrators of those wonderful old Russian novels used to say, 'in a certain area' of London, 'the precise name and location of which need not concern us here.'

'Is that so dreadful?'

'Don't you know it?'

'I do not.'

'Have you never heard of it?'

'I don't think so.'

It was part of the established game between us, one of the conditions that allowed us to meet regularly as acquaintances in London yet never have any other kind of contact with each other, that I should play the role of distanced aesthete and he the informed man about town.

'It must be lovely living up there in the frozen north,' he said. 'All warm and cosy in your snowy ivory tower.'

'We don't have ivory towers in Edinburgh. Not educational ones, anyhow. And if we did, they wouldn't be covered with snow because Edinburgh doesn't get much of that either. As for habitation, we have to make do with either our very own decaying Scottish tenements or pre-cast concrete and glass boxes just like yours. If anything, our buildings are even uglier than yours, I would imagine.'

Derek was unmoved.

'I doubt whether they're uglier than Trevor's.' he murmured. 'That wouldn't really be possible. His place is, quite literally, mid-Victorian. A hospital, once upon a time, and still recognizable as such. It was even functioning as one until a few years ago. The local authority is buying up as many nearby houses as it can get its hands on. Loads and loads of mean streets full of them. They want to drive the locals out and take over before the middle classes move in. It's something of a pity really. Well, I think so. If the middle classes really are always rising, as we're endlessly assured they are, then at least the houses would be restored and maintained. The university is mad keen to pull them all down and build some of those concrete and glass cages you seem so happy to tolerate. I suppose that one day it might be quite cheerful. Meanwhile it's a dilapidated slum hospital masquerading as a dilapidated slum polytechnic surrounded by row upon row of dilapidated terraces. It's remarkably awful.'

Then, leaning forward and returning to his conspiratorial mode, he whispered, 'You know the kind of place. It's financed by the British taxpayer, but they say locally that it takes its orders from Albania.'

Now he did have my attention. I was no clearer whereabouts in London he meant, but I did understand what he was talking about. I couldn't be expected to have any personal experience of such a place, though it would know of me and be eager to keep me at arm's length. That much was clear, though it didn't explain why one of them might want to contact me. Surely they would be too narrowly set in their ways for anything like that. An ideological error, perhaps? An instance of misidentification? I'd had some of those before.

They were a nuisance, but they usually came from young and inexperienced research students and the initial confusion was soon cleared up. During a brief chat over a couple of pints, I would make it plain that although I had written quite a bit about the portrayal of the poor and working classes in fiction, I was not involved in any kind of planning for a working-class revolution. Nor did I much relish the thought of one ever taking place. That settled, individual positions were reasserted, and we parted speedily and with no serious damage done, apart from me probably having made yet another enemy. The occasions themselves were generally friendly with little embarrassment caused. Even so, it didn't sound as though the present instance fitted into that pattern.

Derek's description of the polytechnic's local reputation was clearly his own colourful gloss. People living locally would never have thought of any educational institution in such terms. They were more likely to be delighted to have an expanding polytechnic nearby whatever its political tone and be looking forward to the rise of employment levels and living standards it would bring with it. But Derek knew perfectly well what message he wanted to convey, and so did I.

'And what does he want with me?'

'I've no idea. I was in the Museum Arms just before Christmas. There were half a dozen of us, including Trevor. I had never met him before. Your name came up. It was to do with one of your reviews in the *TLS*, and I said something about you being in the BM fairly regularly. When we were all leaving, Trevor took me aside and asked if I really did know you personally, and if so could I introduce him to you. He was very impressed. He said he knew your work *very* well. There was a *very* heavy emphasis on the *verys*. It was rather humbling for me. I could feel a little of your stardust glitter tumbling over my unworthy populist shoulders.'

'He didn't say anything else?'

'No. I suggested he write to you at Edinburgh, but he didn't fancy doing that. He seemed a bit worried by the old pen and paper. So I said how about me organizing a tea party when you were next down? That he did take to. He doesn't seem to have picked up a sense of irony from his sojourns at the Round Table. Perhaps they didn't have any irony in those days, or tea parties either come to that. I managed to persuade him that an actual tea party might, after all, be a little troublesome, and he settled for me contacting him when you were next around. And here you are. Shall I give him a ring?'

We arranged to meet the next day in the same café at much the same time. I was there first. Derek came in with Trevor, introduced us politely and formally to each other, said, 'Well, I'll leave you to it,' and was gone before I had even a chance to invite him to stay. Not that I particularly wanted him to hang around, though I did feel he might have managed his part in the affair with a little more grace. The abruptness of his departure demanded a comment of some kind.

'Diplomatic?' I suggested.

'Fear probably,' Trevor countered.

'Of what?'

'Of getting involved. Commitment. Something of that kind. It's understandable, I suppose. For Derek anyway. Though not for you, I imagine, and certainly not for me either. My problem's exactly the opposite.'

I let that rest. For the moment anyway. It would obviously resurface however I responded. The mention of commitment had been too swift and too deliberate for it not to be some kind of indicator. It wasn't a label I looked forward to talking about. I had got used to thinking of myself not quite as uncommitted but detached, and yet here was someone I hadn't heard of until yesterday telling me I wasn't actually any such thing. And perhaps he was right. I was certainly committed in some ways, committed to the point of enslavement. Not in the usual political sense, though, but to certain ideals, my project, to a type of personal achievement. And Derek? Ostensibly so successful, so pushy, who spent the greater part of his days drifting, floating, swooping raptor-like on visitors to the Reading Room, collecting people to draw from them whatever information they might possess, twisting and turning, constantly on the lookout for some kind of personal advantage. A special kind of commitment? Or was it fear? It was hard to say, but perhaps Trevor was right. On the other hand, Trevor himself being too committed was quite obviously the text for the day. He had proclaimed it as such even before I had had time enough to go to the counter to fetch him a cup of coffee. There was no way I could know what he meant, and I wasn't sure I wanted to be enlightened. All I could do was wait for clarity.

I was used to academics talking in code. An alternative to ordinary speech was necessary because virtually everything they had to communicate was learned from someone else and shared out among themselves, barely ever their own. If true to form, any explanation from Trevor of what we were doing together would have to be left to emerge at its own pace and in Academese, a language I was at least capable of understanding.

Meanwhile, there was a more immediate problem to be considered. Simply by walking into the café, Trevor had presented me with a puzzle. I hadn't quite believed Derek when he said he hardly knew Trevor, or at least I had felt it unlikely to be completely true. Derek knew everyone, immediately, intuitively. In my experience he had no equal in placing people slickly and precisely on a social and cultural scale. It was his skills with this kind of thumbnail sketch, honed in the Reading Room and then dressed up with semi-scholarly facetiousness, that had made him a success as a critic and interviewer on BBC radio. But on this occasion his skills seem to have been lacking in some way or other because he hadn't prepared me at all for the man I was now sitting opposite.

Trevor was what my mother would have described as well set up, her model being British film stars of the 1940s and 1950s before they were overthrown by the more casual working-class images of the Sixties. He was tall, slim, good looking in a carefully groomed manner, and roughly the same age as me, perhaps a year or two older. There was something of the off-duty army officer about him, formal but at the same time relaxed. His hair was very light brown and smartly combed, though floppy as well. He was wearing a double-breasted blazer decorated with brass buttons, a white shirt and a tie of light blue and amber stripes. There were other people around in 1981 dressed like Trevor and no doubt there still are. But in higher education? Perhaps a former serviceman on the administrative side, someone used to directing unruly undergraduates into paths that were presumed to be good for them, but not a lecturer, not a specialist in Arthurian legends, not the inhabitant of a north London polytechnic that was far enough to the Left for Derek Wisthrop to refer to it with contempt. It was all rather strange. Or perhaps I was guilty of indulging in a bit of all too easy stereotyping. Still, at least half of the stereotype seemed to fit.

For me, going to the trouble of asking someone like Derek to arrange a meeting of this kind would have been impossible to contemplate, the potential complications too great to bother with. I could only have gone through with it if driven by an urgent personal crisis, but already I could see that for Trevor it would simply be a task to be done, a familiarity with decision-making at one with the semi-official manner of his dress. Straight and to the point I assumed, a man used to being in charge. Having decided on me, and got me, he would be eager to push on. I rather expected him to bark out some order or other, but his opening gambit was quietly insinuating.

'What do you think of St John-Stevas?' he asked

I was instantly on guard, disappointed, even annoyed. 'What do you think of someone or other?' is the common opening conversational gambit employed by one academic to another, usually about the work of a third. It's the standard starting point of lengthy tedious discussions, sometimes worthy, more often catty, and usually pointless. It was an approach I spent a good deal of time trying to avoid and here I was caught up in one. Perhaps my stereotyping had been totally wrong after all. Was this why Derek had put the two of us together and then rushed off out of the way? I was instantly suspicious. What on earth had he been doing to get me stuck here with the kind of academic he must have known I would have no interest in meeting? It seemed impossible to get up and leave as I suddenly wanted to. Instead, I decided to suffer one or two moves, and then be off as fast as possible.

At least the name Trevor had presented to me was unexpected and not awkwardly departmental or subject-based. And surely it was distinctive enough for there not to be too many of them about. The St John-Stevas who came to mind was pretty well unique and could hardly be the person Trevor meant. I tried it though.

'*Norman* St John-Stevas?'

'Yes.'

'The Bagehot man?'

'Well, yes of course. Not that it was Bagehot I had in mind.'

He paused for a moment, amused by some connection his own words had started up in him, and added. 'Come to think of it, though, it could well have been, couldn't it?'

I had no idea why it could or couldn't have been, though the Bagehot man it clearly was. *Walter* Bagehot, the leading Victorian authority on constitutional matters. On my shelves at home I had several of his books: a cheap late Victorian reprint of *The English Constitution* (1867); a two-volume Everyman's Library edition of *Literary Studies* which contained his once renowned comparison of Tennyson and Browning; and a more recently published study of him, part biography, part anthology, part exposition. The author of this book was Norman St John-Stevas who was also responsible for the publication of an ongoing multi-volume edition of Bagehot's complete works. It was an endeavour that would have brought prestige and promotion to an ambitious scholar, the kind of project that very few individuals not backed by university funding would have even have attempted since Bagehot's own time. But this

Norman St John-Stevas wasn't an academic. He was a Member of Parliament, and a media celebrity; always snappily dressed, a public spokesman for Catholicism and the Monarchy, a TV pundit and wit, a Victorian who had somehow survived into the twentieth century.

'*Norman St John-Stevas?*' I asked again.

'Yes. I was wondering how you felt about him. About him going?'

I might have been tempted to respond with a corny joke if Trevor hadn't looked so earnest. But what worked well enough with Derek's codified talk clearly wasn't appropriate here. I admitted to not understanding the question.

'I'm sorry. Haven't you heard? It is in all the papers. Rather prominently so.'

I explained that I hardly ever read newspapers, and that as the last day or so had been taken up with travelling down from Edinburgh and settling in London I was cut off from late-night television, my usual source of information about current affairs.

Trevor raised his eyes slightly as though not quite approving of what I had said. The gesture, though barely perceptible, marked a change in his manner. Perhaps I was turning out to be a surprise to him as well. I was conscious of him observing me, preparing himself, I imagined, for having to admit he had made a mistake. Perhaps it was his turn to consider pushing his coffee cup to one side and saying with exaggerated politeness, how nice it had been to meet me but unfortunately he had to go. He didn't do it, though, any more than I had a few minutes earlier. Instead, he provided me with a current update.

In addition to appearing on television and radio and regularly bringing out volumes of Bagehot, St John-Stevas was a member of Margaret Thatcher's recently formed cabinet, a busy one at that. He was Leader of the House and minister responsible for the Arts. As a natural publicist he was also something of a self-appointed spokesman for the new political age. An attractive, witty, useful advocate, I would have thought, for a new government with such a heavy image. But no longer, it seemed. Two days earlier, at about the same time that I was boarding a train at Waverley, he had been sacked. It was an act, Trevor said, that had deeply shocked St John-Stevas. And other people too. After all, he was a good man. Caring, intelligent, scholarly, perfectly fitted for the posts to which he had been appointed. Didn't I agree?

Yes, I said, yes I did. I wasn't all that more interested in political ups and downs than I was in their academic equivalents, but it had seemed to me a rare and welcome move for a government to appoint as minister for the Arts someone who actually knew something about them.

'Why was he sacked?'

'Nobody's quite sure. It doesn't make a lot of sense unless he's being used as a sacrificial victim. Stretched out on the altar of political necessity. You know the sort of thing.'

'Is that what the papers are saying?'

'No, not yet. They're thrashing about, busily personalizing the whole affair, claiming that Mrs Thatcher was upset by his patrician manner. They say he was rude to her and he might well have been, though not consciously I'm sure. Others are saying he was incompetent, and a leaker to boot. That, of course, would be a more serious offence. I don't think I believe any of it.'

He smiled, to himself more than me, as he considered the possible causes of St John-Stevas's downfall, and added, 'Mind you, I don't suppose that jibe about the "Blessed Margaret" could have done him much good. But who knows?'

'And where does the idea of him being a sacrificial victim come from?'

'I rang a constituency friend of mine as soon as I heard the news.'

Once again I was set wondering whether Derek could have known anything whatsoever about Trevor when he introduced us. What kind of person was it who spoke so confidently about his 'constituency'? Who had friends they could ring to check on the accuracy of news reports? No one I knew, and surely not anyone working at the kind of polytechnic that had been described to me. It all felt far too incongruous to be true, and so it was. As I learned later, Trevor's constituency, by which he meant the place where he lived and voted, as well as being the embodiment of his political beliefs, was an extremely well-heeled part of suburban Middlesex. For the moment, though, I was confused.

'How is it that this friend of yours knows things the papers don't?' I asked.

If my question carried a gentle note of scepticism with it, as I had rather intended it to, Trevor took no notice.

'It's not really a matter of knowing, is it?' he replied calmly, once again seemingly puzzled by my naivety on such matters. 'Understanding, rather. Or, even better, being aware of possibilities.'

Then, slowly and hesitantly, he said, 'There are some people who believe that big changes are coming. And when I say big, I mean it. Big. Perhaps I shouldn't announce them as a certainty, as though we can rely on them arriving by Tuesday week at the latest. That's not the way things are. In fact, it's only fair to say there are some influential people who believe that nothing very much is going to happen at all, that it's all bluff, a storm destined to blow itself out. They are even beginning to act as though the bluff has already been called. But others, with my constituency friend among them, say that they're the ones who are being bluffed. And St John-Stevas is close to them, the wets I mean. He's one of the not yet converted. And he's hardly alone in that. It all depends…'

Trevor had run into silence, temporarily unwilling or unable to spell out the kind of conversion he had in mind. I tried prompting him.

'On what?' I asked, 'I mean, what does it depend *on*?'

'The Lady. The "Blessed Margaret." I was there, you know, at Brighton in October. It was amazing. "You turn if you want to," he quoted dreamily. "The Lady's not for turning." Isn't it remarkable that we have a prime minister, a Conservative of the deepest blue, who can say such a thing? And, cross fingers, she might even mean it. The trouble is everything still has to be worked for, the way prepared.'

'Sacrifices made,' I murmured, imagining St John-Stevas dressed in his customary pinstriped suit, deep blue shirt and cutaway white collar, bound to the altar of political necessity, while Margaret Thatcher, adorned in the billowing robes of an Ayesha-style high priestess, stood poised above him, knife in hand, ready to strike, laying the ground for hitherto unthinkable political change.

'Yes,' Trevor nodded ruefully, still struggling to adjust his own mind to St John-Stevas's sudden departure from the cabinet. 'Yes, that's about it.'

'But if he's so good at his job why does he need to go?'

'Well, that's exactly the point. It's supposed to be alien to us, isn't it? Not, of course, to some of our colleagues, yours and mine, but you know this as well as I do. There's nothing they like better than the thought of sacrificing individuals to large causes. They relish the thought. They would just love to be personally involved in the necessary action. I've no doubt they spend every night in their comfy beds dreaming blissfully of the chance which, of course, they are never going to get, thank God! And they don't stick at the odd disposable politician. Numbers are irrelevant. The more the merrier. But not us. We don't believe in such behaviour, do we? We're like Hedda Gabler. We're not supposed to "do such things." But she did. That's Ibsen's point. And why shouldn't it be ours as well? What's holding us back?'

'Lacking in confidence,' Derek had said. 'Probably weak.' That was beginning to seem as wrong as it was possible for one person to be about another. I agreed with Trevor about left-wing academics, their careless attitude to ordinary life, and the theoretical ruthlessness on behalf of a working class that most of them had barely any personal experience of. But were they so different from us? From Trevor and me, that is.

As he was so obviously right that they were never going to be in a position of real power or influence, what difference could there be between them and us that amounted to anything more than a rhetorical flourish? That was a position I had long held, and I had done so fully aware that it was at odds with my idealism in many other areas of life. However different our political views, it seemed to me that we were all mired in the shameful purposelessness of British politics that apart from a few remarkable, and fleeting, years of reconstruction immediately after the Second World War, was the only thing my generation had ever known. Nobody, as far as I could see, wanted anything to do with it, except perhaps the Liberals who, after long years of being dismissed as irrelevant to this and most other issues, were beginning to strut about a little and announce they were going to take control of something they called the centre of British politics. Maybe! They'd have to find it first. And it surely wasn't just the Right that was calling for an end to U-turns. Who believed more strongly than the far Left in a straight undeviating road ahead? The destination they dreamed of may have been as unreal as Trevor said, but their longing for purposeful action wasn't. I'd always supposed it was precisely because they were determined not to be turned that their supporters were so few, so dedicated, and capable of nothing but symbolic acts. Not the rest of us, though, with our multi-shaded beliefs, veering in various degrees left or right. Wobble was the only item on the agenda.

'Shouldn't it be who?' I asked.

'I beg your pardon?'

'Shouldn't it be who rather than what is holding you back? The Lady?'

'I'm not sure,' Trevor muttered. 'No, I don't think so. Not any longer.'

We had both temporarily slipped so far away into our own thoughts that he might have nodded off after his earlier vigour. He was like someone being roughly woken up, asking himself where exactly he was, shaking his head gently to get rid of a lingering drowsiness, unwilling to confront whatever it was would have to be done once consciousness returned.

Then, as though having rubbed the sleep from his eyes, he said firmly: 'Perhaps we have to give up all this nonsense of asking *who* people are and where they are on the social scale. We should start paying more attention to what they really want or are willing to support. In my particular world, we're all so concerned with *placing* people that we often fail to get through to the individual. We have to move beyond all that. After all, it's the extraordinary fluidity of our world that weakens us as well as saves us.'

I wasn't sure I understood what Trevor was saying. The bit about fluidity seemed to make sense, but what was his 'particular world'? Not that I was going to be enlightened, for the moment anyway. Whatever priorities Trevor had settled on during his dreamy meditation, he seemed happy to keep them to himself. The only clear result to have emerged from it was that in the last twenty minutes or so he had somehow brought himself round to agreeing with his leader that poor St John-Stevas would have to be cast into political obscurity.

* * * *

By now it was well after five o'clock and our attention was being drawn to more mundane matters than high politics. The sole member of staff in the café was rather noisily tidying up. It was only when he lifted the cups and saucers from our table with a gentle reminder that he should have closed ten minutes ago that we realized we were marooned, the last surviving customers. We rose hurriedly, flustered at the inconvenience we were causing and at the same time disappointed at having to move at all.

It was Trevor who proposed a solution. A little wine bar near Holborn tube station. It would be fairly quiet at this time of the evening, though busier later with people from Lincoln's Inn Field. Would I share with him a bottle of Beaujolais-Villages, a speciality of the bar, always in perfect condition? No, certainly not, he wouldn't think of it. I was *his* guest. Definitely. No arguments, please. He owed me, he said. If, of course, I could spare the time.

I could do that all right but I would have to go back to the BM first and clear my neglected desk. Trevor had some things to pick up as well, so we made our way together through the Museum courtyard now empty of tourists; in and out of the Reading Room which as usual this time of the evening was bidding farewell to its daytime readers and welcoming in its evening regulars; then out again to face the clangorous traffic of Southampton Row.

The wine bar was in a narrow lane running off of High Holborn which I had never before noticed, and it did produce for us, as Trevor had promised, a truly luscious Beaujolais. There were few other customers and we settled ourselves at the corner of a long wooden table that occupied one side of the room. Trevor poured the wine, raised his glass in a silent toast, and leaned back in his chair, inviting me to restart our conversation which I was ready enough to do.

'What is it,' I asked, tapping my wine glass,' that this is payment for? You said you owed me.'

He grinned shyly, making me aware that in the couple of hours since we had met this was the first time he had displayed any kind of lightness of spirit. Though even now the moment was one of personal awkwardness rather than humour, just a slight lessening perhaps of his distinctive air of self-control. I had no idea what it was he was controlling, but I was confident he had manoeuvred me into asking my question and was ready to answer it.

'Isn't it obvious what I owe you? ' he said. 'You could say, reasonably enough, that I'm an admirer, a fan even. I'm indebted to you for your support. Steadily and consistently given over, well, the past ten years or so, I imagine it must be.'

I wasn't ready for this.

'What kind of support?' I asked.

He paused long enough for me to tilt my head enquiringly at him before continuing. His words were not exactly prepared, but they had certainly been long considered.

'I'm an inhabitant of the waste land,' he explained, 'waiting for the rains to arrive and all that. Like you, I earn my living by teaching people to read literature, or, as it feels for me much of the time, simply teaching people to read. Like you, I'm fascinated by the historical and political implications of what I'm teaching. No one else in my department shares those interests. Some of my colleagues even deny that literature can properly concern itself with ideas of any kind, beyond I suppose a generalized personal and social morality. They're happy enough to exist in a literary world that is all but entirely unconscious of anything but itself, whatever that may be. I don't want to follow them down that path and I have no alternative outlet because my favoured ground has been occupied entirely by the Left. There's nowhere for me to go. I'd like to take the battle to them if that were possible, but it isn't. They have created my waste land. They are the drought that makes resurrection so unlikely. For me, I mean, but not apparently for you. You seem to have found a way out of this kind of impasse. In your books and in your reviews as well. It's odd. You write about the same kind of things as they do, even about other things they might be expected to write about but don't, and you do so from a very different point of view. That point of view is mine as well. I've no idea how you do it, but you do, and I'm grateful.'

I asked why, if he felt it to be so important, he couldn't join me. 'Not,' I added, 'that I personally think of these things in the same way as you. There's no secret about my approach, no definable theory or method. I'm an empiricist, and that's all. What some regard as a dirty word for a dirty activity. I stand apart and observe, try to see what is there before me, and take no notice of what, academically at least, is going on around me. I simply get on with my work.'

'That's instinct,' he replied, 'not an approach. And I don't think I'd agree that you're some kind of innocent empiricist. You don't seem very removed or neutral to me, and I'm glad you're not. As for my position. Well, it's hardly unique. You must know plenty of academics like me who are pushing forty and have never published anything of note. In my case hardly anything. A few articles, that's about it. For people who are happy to accept being in that kind of situation it must be rather pleasant. But I can't. I'm always aware of what I would have liked to be doing, or rather what I should have been doing, and for some reason or other can't. It makes me guilty. It's like driving accidentally into a cul-de-sac and finding there's not enough room to turn round. If I started to make a fuss about being where I am I'd appear ridiculous, trapped by my own foolishness. I could buckle down and write a book on Malory's knights. In some ways I'd love to do that. But the battles would all be in the book. Plus, of course, the odd running skirmish with the two or three other people in the academic world who would also love to write a book about Malory's knights. But you're engaged in a battle all of the time, whether you acknowledge it or not. That's why they dislike you.'

'And ignore me.'

'Not quite. And anyway it doesn't matter, does it? The two things go together. Being ignored is an expression of their special kind of blindness. Their shocking unwillingness to allow alternatives to exist. You're *there* to be ignored. That's the important bit. It's an achievement. It takes a conscious effort. I'm not even part of the scene.'

I suppose it was the appearance of this self-effacing side of Trevor that allowed me to frame the question I most wanted to ask. He was right, of course, that there were plenty of university teachers around in his kind of career situation, and right as well that most of them weren't personally attracted by left-wing doctrine. And they got on perfectly well without it. But if, like Trevor, they did regard their literary studies as pushing them towards some kind of political or social debate, what alternatives did they have? My go-it-alone solution could mean nothing to them. They were more likely to not get involved at all. Into my mind there floated the words of one of the great Scottish moles of modern fiction, trying to break through a similar kind of group intimidation, though of a rather different persuasion: 'Have you thought of politics, Miss Mackay?' No, of course she hadn't until the option was put to her. Nor had they. As Trevor had just said, they had allowed themselves to be driven underground by the pervasive leftist atmosphere of university campuses, persuading themselves that politics were none of their business. In the process they had encouraged a vocal minority to strut around, promoting a fake radical agenda that curiously enough had no significant influence whatever on the staid conservative institutions that universities essentially are. Like Miss Mackay, they needed waking up, to be made aware of the reality of the power base they occupied instead of fecklessly handing it over for others to set the tone.

Trevor obviously didn't need wakening up, but then he had been quick to confess that he felt unable even to try to change the situation. He'd suggested I must know lots of people in his kind of position? Well, I did and I didn't. My usual response when anything like this arose was one of withdrawal, telling myself, and them as well if forced to do so, that their dilemma was entirely up to them to sort out. That wasn't exactly sympathetic and probably not very helpful either, but what else could I do? I wasn't in the business of giving advice. Not that Trevor needed any. He was fully conscious of his outcast state, so aware of what it meant to be politically trapped in the waste land of Academia, that he might have been preparing to turn our situations entirely around and start advising me. None of it quite fitted together.

For a start there wasn't motive enough in that unwritten book on the knights errant to carry the weight Trevor gave it. I was beginning to feel there had to be something else tucked away, another side of the story. Or perhaps I was simply hoping there was. If not, there could yet be a worrying familiarity to all of this. My earlier doubts about Trevor were once again making themselves felt. Could I really have unwittingly volunteered to have foisted upon me the dreary details of yet one more dead-end academic career? It was only because I made a desperate move to shift myself away from that possibility that I learned how wrong I was.

'Why now?' I asked abruptly. 'At this present moment, I mean?'

He was delighted with my question, visibly so.

'Ah, well,' he replied, as though thankful at last to be asked and, barely holding back a childish giggle. 'What a pertinent thing to ask for someone who claims to be so out of touch. Unfortunately there's no simple answer. Not at the moment anyway. Just conflicting areas of concern, as it were. There's the St. John Stevas syndrome, about which, thanks to you, I think I'm beginning to see a little more clearly, and then ...' He paused, ran the tip of his tongue lightly, playfully around his top lip, and added slowly, 'there's my own situation.'

With that my fear of the wine bar being turned into an academic confessional disappeared and our temporarily stalled conversation, already relaxed by the wine and the unspoken understanding that another bottle would follow whenever it was needed, prepared itself to move on.

We were helped in this by the bar filling up with people on their delayed journeys home from the offices in and around Lincoln's Inn. To make it possible for a party of some eight or ten to sit together, we were asked if we would mind moving to a smaller table tucked away in a far corner which we happily did. We were now set a little apart from the bustling middle of the room, framed by a velvet-curtained window on one side and an increasing press of standing customers on the other. Around us there were a few other couples – furtive lovers and office plotters in the main, I guessed – who had also retreated willingly or been shifted to the fringes of the room. By the time I made my way through the crowded centre of the bar and then back again with the second bottle of wine we were like old friends, able to drop and pick up on our conversation effortlessly.

It turned out that Trevor wasn't actually teaching at the polytechnic that Derek, though never Trevor himself, I noticed, thought so little of. Otherwise the general drift of Derek's information had been correct. The polytechnic *did* exist, it *was* busily buying up whatever property it could lay its hands on in the neighbouring area and sometime in the future it was going to buy up Trevor as well. For the past ten years or so he had been teaching in a small further education college, a remnant it seemed of the days when teachers were taught in their own dedicated colleges. He said that as higher education had become increasingly centralized, places like his were often thought to have faded completely away. But not yet they hadn't. Apparently a surprising number of them lingered on, serving local communities, providing qualifications for students caught between school and higher education, running vocational courses, meeting many of the aspirations that were now more commonly catered for by the Open University. Eventually these anomalous institutions would be absorbed by nearby polytechnics. Trevor and his colleagues at the college were to be transferred once their present diploma courses were completed. They expected this to be in three years time. Perhaps a bit longer. It wasn't yet clear when exactly.

He knew that for years he'd been spoilt, knew it, knew it all too well. How could he possibly object to his college being closed down? It was good enough for the mopping up the local council wanted it to do. Far too good really. But the place had been haemorrhaging money for years, indefensibly so. There was no point now in him saying that he might have moved on when he had had the chance. Yes, of course he *might* have done. Back in fatter years he could perhaps have found a university gullible enough to believe that another book on Malory was greatly needed and that he was the man to meet the demand. Goodness, he laughed, now obviously enjoying himself, once safely installed he might even have written the book! Even so, he liked his present job. Liked it a lot. He was good at it and got on well with the miscellaneous students who over the years had drifted to his college for help. But the truth was that personally he didn't really want any of it. Not deep down he didn't. He was where he was because he *had* no academic ambitions or drive, and he'd never much bothered about that because he hadn't expected to stay in teaching, let alone look to it for a career. Nor did he want the polytechnic where he knew he would be treated as a political leper. 'Still, it might never happen,' he muttered, more to himself than to me. 'It doesn't have to.'

This was all on the downside, and I waited for more. The slightly querulous tone he had slipped into didn't feel characteristic of him. If, at heart, he really didn't care about the academic life, then why care about being forced to leave it? Simply losing a cushy job couldn't be the issue, not in his case. There had to be something else. Meanwhile I hadn't failed to notice that to a surprising extent Trevor had been describing my own situation, my feelings, as well as his, though he himself couldn't possibly have known it. If I had interrupted him at this point he might well have responded with something like, 'well, it's all right for you.' And I suppose it was. In his terms. Though not in mine.

According to what are generally taken to be very wise words, we should all be careful of what we wish for in life because it might be granted unto us. I had longed to be buried by books, with just enough air coming through to allow me to read and to write about as many of them as possible. My wish had been granted and, although not consciously planned, along with it had arrived a guaranteed academic post at a reputable university, with pretty well as much additional prestige as I cared to go for. The trouble was I didn't want to go for it. I didn't even want much of what I already had. Just the books and the means to write about them without the accompanying complications of living in such an uncaring environment. It was a ridiculous position to be in, a trap I had closed upon myself. I was beginning to feel like the beautiful, pampered, unsatisfied bird in a gilded cage that my grandmother had loved to sing about. It was true enough, for outsiders it would have all looked perfectly all right for me.

Not that Trevor was preparing to say anything like this. For a moment I had feared he might be, but he wasn't. Instead, he raised his head, stared at me just a trifle defiantly and announced: 'I had my chance, though. Not much of one as things turned out. But, there we are. A chance of sorts, and a real one.'

And without pausing he relived that chance for me.

* * * *

A few years ago, he began, 'when Edward Heath was losing an election by giving in to the unions and Harold Wilson was winning one by shamelessly buying them off,' he had been selected as the parliamentary Conservative candidate in a by-election. The constituency was in the west Midlands and as far as his party was concerned something of lost cause. It was a mixed working and middle-class area with a growing number of immigrants, a fairly safe Labour seat. Before the war, though, it had been strongly Conservative and there was a feeling inside the party that it could be taken back. Not, though, 'as long as Ted was in charge.' The problem, apparently, was that the Party had two agendas which were beginning to clash with each other. There was one for the faithful few (and thought not sufficiently attractive to make public) and another that was safe enough to put forward but wasn't proving attractive anyway. Even if you can win an election on those principles, or lack of them, what good does it do? It was gradually coming to be understood that Ted was the problem.

'Once when I was out canvassing, ringing bells, knocking on doors; a ginormous blue rosette pinned to my lapel, leaflets at the ready, supported by a visitor from Central Office and a handful of local party workers, the owner of one of the houses answered the bell, and when he saw which party I represented he totally ignored my outstretched hand and whatever polite inanities I was uttering. He just stood on the doorstep, silently, a ghastly grin fixed across his face, his shoulders bouncing up and down. He never said a word, but stepped back into the house, maintaining his cartoon pose the whole time, and very slowly closed the door on me. He might have been one of those little manikins in a German clock, announcing the time by stiffly emerging from his cage and just as stiffly retreating back into it.'

My move to express sympathy was swept away.

'Oh no,' Trevor said cheerfully. 'That was it. The end. I knew it. But, it was one of those ends that are important. Inspiring, actually. From that moment I knew, we all knew, that thanks to Ted there would be no more fake agendas. That will go down in history as his great achievement. He made it certain that the next time we would make a real fight of it on policies that mattered. To us, and to the country.'

Trevor came third in the poll, beaten even by a 'pathetic Liberal.' In the early hours of a warm May morning, he had stood on a platform in a crowded town hall listening to the public announcement of his political humiliation. He was in a part of the country where he'd never been before and had hardly known existed until he had been sent up there to be slaughtered. The local party officials gathered around him, protecting and nurturing their candidate, having known all along that he had no chance of winning. Most of them shared his distaste for Wilson and his lack of faith in Heath. When, in a speech during the campaign, he had condemned the miners for acting as though they were an elected government, Central Office issued him with a rebuke but his party helpers cheered wildly and called for more. All they were thinking about, he explained, was the next time or perhaps the time after that. But, whenever it might be, they knew it would come. They were in waiting.

I must say it didn't sound all that inspiring to me. Trevor's faith, though, was unchecked. In the Midlands he had discovered inextinguishable hope, a dedicated agent and eager helpers. Everywhere around him there was common passion and companionship. True camaraderie. It was unlikely, he admitted sadly, that the experience would be repeated.

The constituency which he believed could still be won wanted him back for the 1979 General Election, but the party had sent someone else. Although the new candidate hadn't actually taken the seat, he was expected to do so next time. Meanwhile, Trevor had stood for adoption by two other constituencies. Neither had selected him.

He put it all down to timing. He had been a parliamentary candidate when the Conservatives were losing and could cheerfully accept the defeat of enthusiastic candidates in impossible seats. Now they were winning and even the unlikeliest seats were attracting ambitious, well-connected, would-be politicians. Enthusiasm was no longer enough. 'We all know that politicians should never give up,' Trevor said dryly. 'That at least is what people claim. And sure enough there are politicians who have made spectacular comebacks. Mind you, there have been a lot more of the sunk-without-a-trace variety.' He himself hadn't give up entirely, but for the time being had settled for working in the back room, advising others on how to turn his kind of rejection into acceptance, working for both local and national campaigns which he could actively support but which he would probably never again front.

Hearing this I was more than ever aware how differently Trevor must have regarded our two careers. Whatever kind of gloss he put on the experience, he must surely have felt his by-election defeat as another personal failure, a political equivalent to the unwritten Malory book. In comparison, I was the parliamentary candidate who had not only been adopted by a distant constituency but who had then gone on to win the by-election and hold it safely, as it were, with an increased majority in subsequent general elections. Not that it was quite that clear cut. On the hustings we had both had cheers all the way, only to hear them fade away at the final count. It was at that point we parted. Trevor had accepted defeat. I had refused to accept victory. These terms Trevor had agreed with himself to live by. He was part of an institution he could continue to support and admire, and one that always had a welcome place for someone like him.

I had never considered the university as functioning in any way remotely similar to that. For me it was a necessary sanctuary where individualism could flourish. A few successful academics prospered, everyone survived (whether successful or not) and found a pleasant niche for themselves, while the university built for itself a reputation largely out of the activities of the successful few. It was staff I had mainly in mind, but wasn't it much the same for students as well? Perhaps even more rigorously so. After all, their courses were focused in the most harshly competitive of ways and were definitely for a minority. The majority of students either accepted lesser targets or none at all and settled, in varying stages of contentment, for what was on offer, many of them paying little real attention at all to the scholarly or intellectual advantages offered up to them. They needed no convincing that their universities were happily in the business of providing comfort and support for those who weren't idealistically driven.

My view on all of this which had been developed during my early months in Leicester and stayed unchanged ever since, had worked well enough. Too well in some ways. I had allowed myself to accept the personal price of living within an environment I disliked because I was sure that my time as an academic would be short. But things hadn't worked out like that. Early success had meant I was presented with plenty of unwanted opportunities to move up within the system when what I actually wanted to do was to move out of it. Obviously enough the university wasn't going to help me do that. It was my responsibility to find the motive and the means to act, and so far the few opportunities that had presented themselves were either too flimsy to take a risk on, or were not unlike Trevor's political ambitions in the Midlands in having been wrecked by the ghastly economic and political flux of the Seventies.

No doubt there were other academics dotted about here and there in a similarly fortunate position to me, clinging to a productive individualism and being encouraged by their institutions to do just that. Still, far more were consoling themselves with the calmer alternatives on offer, and not necessarily from selfish motives. My path had always been stubbornly clear. I had only ever considered the forms of support that would leave me free to be myself. The easily accessible forms of institutional support I had ignored, and now I was just beginning to wonder whether I had been right to make my stand so inflexibly. Wasn't it just possible that I had left myself with virtually nothing at all to survive on? What Trevor seemed to regard as a huge difference between us, suddenly felt as though it was narrowing rapidly, with the advantage even shifting to his side.

From the moment we had come together earlier that afternoon, there had been an assurance about Trevor, an air of certainty that had both impressed and slightly disturbed me. It was strongly there in spite of the stories he had told of failed ambitions. There was nothing bland about it, no sense of him being over confident on where exactly he stood personally. After all, it had been plain that the sacking of St. John-Stevas had challenged or even shocked him, at first anyway. But he had sought advice on the matter, weighed up the options. And that advice and those options had been readily available for him, even though the internal political battle, as he had described it, was still being fought. It meant choosing between competing sides in a conflict that had been decided for him back in the Midlands a few years earlier. And now those policies were forcing their way onto the front line, justifying his waiting game, demanding a new loyalty. And wasn't I somewhere in all of that as well? What had drawn his attention to me in the first place had been the unturnable course I was set on, and one that he himself aspired to. Or rather, had once aspired to, because even this he now admitted to having become unattainable.

The more I pondered Trevor's sureness in choosing between options and policies, the more aware I became of the fragility of my hold on university life. If, as I suspected, he still harboured regrets for the academic career he had lost out on, then I simply had to try to put him straight, and the only way I could do this was by telling him something of my story in exchange for his. I don't mean in a purely private sense. My personal life would be no more on display than Trevor's had been. It was careers, working lives, that occupied both of our minds, and any revelations from me would need to be like his, a view from inside my own institutional stronghold. The situation wasn't easy for me. I was aware that anything I did say would mean sharing experiences which I had always kept firmly to myself. Never before had I even tried to talk about them with someone else.

Of course the warm embracing atmosphere of the packed High Holborn bar and the second bottle of Beaujolais-Villages were playing their parts in my willingness to speak out, but I was not so entirely lost to the local atmosphere that I didn't find myself wondering why I hadn't done so before. And with the question came the answer. I had pushed it all behind me because I had never considered it to be worth bothering about. That was why. Only now, with someone I hardly knew was I tempted to disclose things that I had hardly ever mentioned to people who were far closer to me. And although Trevor seemed the ideal person to receive whatever confidence I was willing to unload, I still wasn't completely sure he would believe me.

'Take the case,' I began, awkwardly at first, stumbling a bit, talking to myself as much as to Trevor, 'of an academic, a colleague, a professor of sorts let us say, someone I'm obliged to work closely with. Not through any choice of mine, but because of the fragmented nature of university departments. That's the way things are. Hardly an ideal working relationship, not least because he's someone unable to distinguish one idea from another. He's simply incapable of dealing with them. They terrify him. Present him with an idea and he runs from the room screaming in anguish. Obviously this isn't a matter of particular ideas, of preferring this to that or these to those. All ideas are exactly the same to him. He may even have persuaded himself that they don't actually exist. Whether or not, the problem is clearly his. He can't face up to anything that appears to challenge whatever, if anything, he thinks about his own life, or someone else's come to that. Unfortunately ideas do tend to be challenging, and I suppose that at some point in his life he must have decided to shut them out. It's a compulsion, a disease properly speaking, and should be medically treated. In the outside world it probably would be. In its way it's all rather sad. And, something of a disqualification for the job one would have thought, but there we are. It prevents him from writing the kind of authoritative books that professors are supposed to write. Whether they do or not is beside the point, what matters here is that for him it's made impossible by the terror of personal exposure. After all, you can't write even a poor book, professorial or otherwise, without acknowledging that ideas exist. Well, I can't see how you can.'

Trevor was looking a bit puzzled. By my insecure, rambling narrative I imagined. I paused in case he wanted to intervene, but he said nothing and I pushed on.

'Fortunately there are ways out of this problem and my professor was lucky to stumble upon one of them way back. He is involved in a number of editorial projects. Quite a lot, as many as possible, large and small. Some of these projects are collective rather than individual and in order to deal with them he has gathered around him a number of carefully chosen subordinates who are employed either full or part-time by the university and who are unlikely to upset him by having opinions of their own. There are also a number of affiliated Americans who regard the connection as valuable. Not, I imagine, in money terms but in order to boost their CVs and gain credit back home. One or two of them, though, do suffer from that curious American ambition to occupy a Chair in a British university. They use their regular visits to hawk themselves around. All in all, whether home grown or American, they're a pretty low-key crowd. They function as a clique rather than a working team, a cell operating within the department, on its own terms and according to its own beliefs, establishing its own values, shutting off the possibility of any outside challenge. Do you recognize anything?'

Trevor said he could see what I was getting at, and added. 'Though I think you could drop the "my professor." It is rather cumbersome. Doesn't he have a name? And I must say that I can't see what objection you can possibly have to editorial projects, whether large or small. They're an important part of academic life.'

I assured him I had nothing whatsoever against academic editions, large or small. Or editors. Long may they both flourish! But I would like to hold on to 'my professor,' periphrastic though it was, and not use actual names. If Trevor didn't mind. 'After all, this is a genuine case study, not tittle-tattle. So, will it be all right if I just call him mp?' I asked.

Trevor agreed it would be fine, 'as long as you're not speaking in capital letters. We don't want to involve any MPs in what looks very much like becoming a tale of deceit and deviousness, do we?'

I replied that those qualities were most definitely involved, but what I had in mind was a representative form of ignorance rather than any individual's personal failings. Still, to protect Trevor's sensitivity on the point, I promised to keep a clear distinction between mp and MP, leaving the politicians alone and abbreviating 'my professor' into a kind of burr. Something like Merrp. Would that do? It might sound a bit odd but the proprieties would be maintained. Fair enough?

Trevor laughingly waved me on and I picked up where I had left off.

'Well, cliques of course are common in all big institutions and it's their nature to work in underhand ways. The editorial work proceeds. Don't worry, there's no complaint there. I won't mention it again. But Merrp uses the clique actively to veil his own inadequacies and to forestall any criticism of himself. Supposed criticism, I should say, because most of it exists only in his own mind. He develops images of people which have no connection with reality, and he circulates these as widely as he dares. But he operates entirely through his trusty dependents and never in public, never openly, never in ways that might be challenged.'

Trevor was looking really puzzled by now, worried even, and I could understand why. I had taken on an unfamiliar role and I wasn't feeling exactly happy with it myself.

'OK?' I asked him.

'So far.'

'Well, to keep this on me, Merrp has convinced himself that I'm a committed Marxist, one of the enemy within, planted in the department by the sort of ideologues you are soon to join and who are very indirectly responsible for bringing the two of us together here over this gorgeous wine. Merrp himself conscientiously propagates this view, offered of course as fact, whenever he gets the opportunity. He carefully urges secrecy on his cronies and the wisdom of following his example and communicating only in code. The American members of the clan are particularly susceptible to that approach. When they're over here on their periodic visits, they can't resist seeking me out, sniffing around this strange creature who is set on destroying their civilization, making oblique comments, asking impertinent questions, referring in deeply significant tones to the work of some of Britain's better known Marxist writers – none of whom, incidentally, I've ever even met – looking for inside information, hoping for indiscretions, living dangerously. They're a particularly nasty lot.'

Trevor made a suitably disbelieving face. Then he grinned uneasily, not sure what exactly I was telling him, concerned, I suspect, that I was testing him with some kind of joke, the purpose or direction of which was inexplicable to him.

'That's it,' I announced. 'That's life from the inside. One version. One small part of it, rather. That's how I live. Some of the time anyway.'

'But how is it possible?' he asked. 'Virtually every word you write expresses the opposite position.'

'So it does. Isn't that the glory and the horror of the case? As I say, Merrp can't tell one "position" from another. Perhaps he doesn't want to, perhaps he's incapable of doing so. He is certainly a very stupid man who decided early on that the surest way to the top of the university tree was to compile as many footnotes as possible. He's malicious as well as stupid, not just towards me, but to those of our colleagues or students who won't pander to his diseased mind. The reasons for targeting them have nothing to do with politics. They are entirely, crazily personal. In my case the reasoning is just as crazy but fiercely political. And I don't know why. Ignorance I suppose.'

'I still don't get it. He would only need to read any of your books or reviews to know how wrong he is.'

'Well that's surely very much to the point. Quite apart from him not *wanting* to be proved wrong on this, who in our world is sufficiently interested in his colleagues to read or conscientiously think about what they write? It may happen if some kind of self-interest is involved, but otherwise hardly ever, I'd say. Who would care enough to do that? I've personally known very few such people. Do your colleagues read you and have a clear idea what you stand for?'

I knew instantly it was a tactless thing to say. It made it seem as though I hadn't listened to anything Trevor had been saying earlier. I'm not sure whether I actually blushed, and the atmosphere in the bar was now too thick with cigarette and cigar smoke for Trevor to see whether I had or hadn't. He wasn't upset by it though. He gave one of his childish giggles and deflected my question with, 'I'm hardly the best person to know the answer to that, am I?'

But he did still have questions of his own to put, and pertinent they were. How did I feel about being maligned in this curious way? Why didn't I just put the situation right with Merrp, explain it to him? It was hard to see how such a misunderstanding could persist. He might well be every bit as stupid or malicious as I said, but everyone else wasn't. The editors who sent me books for review obviously knew where I stood on such matters or they wouldn't have sent them to me. And these Americans. Who were they? Though of course, Trevor admitted thoughtfully, there could be a problem with Americans on political issues. He himself had once attended a lecture by a visiting American academic who replied to a political point being put to him with 'but you see, we don't have ideologies in the States.' Even so...

And even so just about summed up the situation, for both of us. For years I had carefully avoided talking about myself in this way. Having now done so, I was already beginning to feel I had been right all along to leave well alone. Against my normal principles I had gone for what I was usually quick to condemn in others as mindless gossip. Not that I thought of it in those terms. After all, what I had told Trevor was completely true. But then, wasn't that the standard defence of habitual gossips everywhere? Of course it was, and for the moment that hadn't bothered me. Nor did I really want to stop, not just yet. I needed, as it were, to learn more about myself. I had allowed all this stuff to build up behind me for far too long not to follow through on it now.

Trevor seemed stranded. He was struggling to tell me, as politely as he could manage, that he was bewildered. Of course he believed what I was saying. But at the same time he really couldn't see how the situation I had described could be true. Well, not quite that, but how it would be able to persist without being revealed as the stupidity it so obviously was.

And he was right. No one of any interest to me outside of the department, friend or foe, would be taken in by such nonsense for a single minute. If Merrp had been capable of damaging any academic ambitions I might have had, he would certainly have done so. He probably thought that's what he was doing. But he was too feeble to achieve any such effect. I was way ahead of him and his Anglo-American gang, beyond his reach, reliant on him for nothing but the most mundane workings of departmental routine.

'But why on earth don't you confront him, tell him he's wrong?' Trevor asked, the words bursting out of him in what sounded very much like irritation or frustration.

'It's not an option. I've told you he doesn't want to be proved wrong on this or anything else, and anyway he's not capable of rational discussion. When he does say anything, it's studiously oblique. There's nothing to confront him with.'

'You should at least clear the air. What you're talking about is serious misrepresentation. Slander if he spoke out with witnesses present. Libel if he wrote it down which he obviously won't do. And does it matter ultimately whether he's acting deliberately or out of ignorance? You're probably right that he can't actually harm your reputation, but if some people listen to him why not others? You should stop it. Unless...'

He paused briefly, uncertain whether he should say what he had in mind before quickly deciding he would.

'Unless, of course, you don't want to stop it. Is that it?'

I truly can't say whether until now I had ever thought of asking myself that question. And if it had been lingering somewhere in my mind, I wouldn't have put it to myself so bluntly. It involved the kind of personal challenge that is always easier to set aside than face. Only when coming from someone else does it insist on being answered. Once released, the implications behind what Trevor had said tumbled over me, struggling against each other for individual attention. Yes, of course it suited me, this puerile departmental plotting. On so many counts. It represented to perfection the side of academic life I resented being connected with. All those distressingly common academic vices: the unwillingness to see what is plainly in front of you, indifference, crippling narrowness.

Oh yes, it suited me in so many ways, not all of which could be blamed on the rickety, morally corrupt parts of university life. After all, no one else could be held responsible for the detached role I had consciously built up in order to ensure my personal survival. I had long wanted to get out of university life and should have done something about it before now. Trevor, the failed academic, the failed politician, knew perfectly well why he was hanging on. He had, as it were, negotiated acceptable terms. I, though, had hung on without really acknowledging that that was what I was doing or thinking any self-justification was necessary; believing only that all those piles of books were enough.

Trevor's frankness had seriously undermined my detached pose. I felt revealed as a kind of voyeur, someone who had come to enjoy watching the plotters as they conspired away, pointlessly, powerlessly, not knowing they were being observed, believing themselves to be so right when they were actually so wrong, their own silliness exposed at every move. For me they constituted what had become an enjoyable sideshow that I didn't want to interrupt or correct. And, as Trevor had said, they could have no effect on my own work in which, anyway, they took no interest whatever. All I had wanted was to remain free to go on weaving my literary and historical web, striving for shape and pattern, for some kind of understanding of the past and how the past becomes the present. That was the only thing that mattered.

'As I understand it,' Trevor said, 'the position you've staked out for yourself, the same position I've often wished that I myself had long ago taken, is expressed on paper, in your books and reviews. I don't mean it isn't here and now in life as well. Of course it is. That's why it's worth doing. It's the price you're paying that would worry me. The other things, though, are surely of a different order. I mean these departmental battles or rivalries, whatever we call them and however hidden they may be. They're not justifiable in the same kind of way. All right, you can't argue them out, on paper or in the open. But in the open is where they should be, forced out if necessary. There's no alternative. They have to be dealt with in life, and you're not doing that. Are these plotters really causing the trouble, or are you doing a bit of plotting of your own? Of course there are horrors all around both of us that we can't do anything about.'

'You don't have to accept them, though.'

'Well, some of them you do and some you don't. You have to move among and around them, tread warily, make choices. That's how our political system works, and don't we all live by similar rules? I'm surrounded by people with views, and not all of them by any means left wing, that I'd prefer to ignore. But I have to be careful, take my time, wait for priorities to emerge. If necessary, I can rant and rave with the best of them. Some people I know do little else. But it's non-productive.'

'That's not a line that's possible within a university. Universities aren't like governments. I don't have the power to work to change what I don't like, or the time to sit about waiting for it to change.'

'Of course you do. That's what lots of people in your kind of situation are doing all the time. It's just that you don't want to. But the options are there for you. I don't see universities as being all that different from politics, in this respect at least. In both of them you can get involved or stand apart just as you wish. Backing off in politics is usually a self-destructive act. It's probably less so in universities. Still, I wouldn't personally recommend it, and certainly not in your case. It's too dangerous for you personally, too isolating.'

There was little for me to say in response. I felt closed off, and relieved as well. It was rare to partake in such an honest exchange. Yet another blot on all those things that outsiders wrongly believe Academia excels at! And, what's more, to carry from it no negative feelings, no personal resentment, no concern for things said that shouldn't have been. Trevor, I sensed, felt much the same. He leaned forward in his chair and carefully shared between our glasses the small amount of wine remaining in the bottle.

It was clear we had both had our say. Trevor didn't even speak to indicate that time was running out. He simply extended his arm across the table and tapped ruefully on the face of his wristwatch. It was heading towards half past eight, the time he had earlier mentioned when he had to be elsewhere for dinner. It was at a club fairly close by, 'just a few stops on the tube,' and he didn't want to be late. As though going along with our thoughts of leaving, the atmosphere in the bar was changing. Customers who had dropped in after work were being replaced by people beginning a night out, and. the earlier atmosphere of adulterous intrigue and office conspiracy was becoming one of staid legitimacy. We accepted the situation and moved to the door.

Outside Holborn tube station Trevor bought an evening paper, glanced at the headlines, then carefully folded it and tucked it under his arm before saying goodbye. Our parting was warm, regretful, and kept slightly formal as well. We told each other how much we had enjoyed our time together and both of us admitted to being unused to such evenings. In spite of the personal warmth, there was no suggestion of a further meeting. We didn't actively rule out the possibility, but nor did we make any of the usual gestures. There was no exchange of home addresses or telephone numbers, no mention of when we might next be working at the BM. We tiptoed around each other on this particular issue, and were aware of doing so. I would probably have put it down to some kind of superstitious feeling that we were better off not pushing our luck if we hadn't discovered that the cause was rooted in yet another quirk we both had.

'I'm no good at keeping in touch,' Trevor muttered, 'I never have been. I wish it wasn't so. But there we are. Not exactly a desirable quality in a would-be politician, is it? The truth is I've come to accept that I don't function all that well out there on my own. I'm happier as part of a team. Today was proof enough of that. I wouldn't have gone ahead and contacted you if it hadn't been for Derek revealing that he knew you. I owe him for that at least.'

I rushed to pick up on the confessional mode, assuring him that he simply couldn't be worse than me. I was the most unreliable correspondent in the whole world. Not in professional or business matters. There was no difficulty there. But for anything personal, I was the worst. Absolutely. In moments of solitary regret, there would creep urgently into my mind vivid images of people I had met fleetingly, liked, and had never met again; those who might have become good friends lost forever; whole phases of my past life left contactless because I just wouldn't put pen to paper in order to keep in touch. Just wouldn't do it. And as for the phone! Well, my happiest moment so far in the technological revolution that we were constantly being told in the early Eighties was unstoppably on the way, was the sudden realization that I was able to switch off the telephone at home whenever I pleased.

And that was how we went our separate ways, with each of us trying awkwardly to outbid the other for the title of the world's most uncommunicative person. And if we made a bit more of a joke of the whole thing than it was actually worth, there was also a larger purpose in the exaggeration because I'm certain we both saw no point in trying to turn the previous four hours into any kind of continuing friendship. Not in any conventional sense there wasn't, not for people like us. What we had achieved actually felt rather more special than that. It was some kind of mutual acknowledgement, reached unexpectedly and unplanned, across our solitary and different yet remarkably similar ways of life. That was unusual enough. There was nothing to be added to it.

At the very last minute, though, Trevor did appear to backtrack on this unspoken agreement.

'Perhaps,' he said suddenly, 'I will try to keep in touch.'

When he caught my look of surprise, he added, 'In one way or another, I mean. No guarantees or anything.' Then grinning in the youthful, slightly cheeky manner that I'd already come to accept as characteristic of him, he added. 'I could keep you informed. You might need that as you don't read the papers. And there'll be no need for you to respond. No need at all. Really, I *mean* it.'

And mean it he obviously did, though I could make little sense of his 'one way or another,' or even, at the time, begin to understand how any communication between us could be other than reciprocal. There was no time to ask him to explain. Nor, as things turned out, was clarification necessary because he did make an effort to keep in touch, and his way of doing so was suitably idiosyncratic. It involved no more meetings between us, no bottles of wine, no further exchanges of experiences, no British Museum. Although Derek Wisthrop continued to seek me out whenever I stepped inside the Reading Room, even he was unable to clarify this particular mystery. I did ask him once if he had seen Trevor. He was embarrassed at not being up with the news and said that Trevor seemed to have disappeared, that he had probably packed his lance and shield and gone off to join a round table somewhere or other. For me, Trevor didn't quite disappear, though I never saw him again.

* * * *

On returning to Edinburgh I found that not only were a new year and a new academic term both underway, but what felt very much like a new Scotland as well. The familiar lethargy was beginning to fade away, faintly as yet but markedly. As the train moved north through Berwick-upon-Tweed it was no longer like entering a time warp. It was even possible to detect a whiff of something very like reality. Just three years earlier there had been so little indication of Scotland being in a positive mood to act on its own account that a referendum set up by James Callaghan's Labour government had been unable to get forty per cent of the country's registered voters to declare in favour of devolution. The terms of the election had been a bit unorthodox, yet one more case of Scotland being robbed as the losers were quick to claim. And it was true that a majority of those who voted had been in favour of devolution, though a total count of only one in three of all registered voters in Scotland hardly qualified as a ringing endorsement.

Even so, the annoyance arising out of that vote bolstered by the gradual understanding that there was no chance of Scotland obtaining full control of revenues from North Sea oil was having an effect. I had become used to political events in Scotland being reflections of actions initiated in England. Rarely did they feel home-grown. This was hardly

England's fault. It was difficult to see how local issues could have the power to function as any kind of force for change while the everyday atmosphere in Scotland remained an all-pervading, ill-defined sniping at everything English. Hiding behind petty snubs and insults was never going to work. The deadening weight of resentment only served to deflate or postpone positive action. But that mood was changing. Suddenly current events were as relevant in Scotland as in England.

The main cause of the change was clear. What had long been needed, the essential catalyst, was a powerful English hate figure to provide a focus for all the self-defeating negativity, someone to galvanize Scotland into action on its own account. This was now made available in the form of Trevor's sacrificial knife-wielding heroine Margaret Thatcher. She was a huge and wonderful gift from the old enemy. No single English leader since Oliver Cromwell had done so much for Scottish unity. Their methods may have been rather different, but the mood they left behind them was similar, with Cromwell's brutal military conquests giving way to economic and social ideas that were every bit as unpalatable to the vast majority of Scots. If Thatcher had actively gone out of her way to separate Scotland from England her success could not have been more decisive. She was perfect for the job.

That I was quick to pick up on all of this was a sign that my own political awareness was beginning to change. It hadn't needed Trevor to remind me that my inclinations had long been conservative, though not affiliated, as his so firmly were to the Conservative party. I was too cut off socially and personally for that to be possible. If I had tried to define my political views more closely, I suspect I would have ended up with a form of radical Toryism that was literary rather than institutional; a cultural idealism of a kind that would never be placed before an electorate; dreamy aspirations that had no connection with the bleak reality of Trevor's doorstep electioneering.

There was one thing, though, we had agreed on. Throughout Britain in the 1970s party politics had become little more than variations on a now distant post-war consensus. There was a growing conviction that it would be healthier for everyone if the policies of the two main parties were more differentiated. As Trevor had discovered on the stump, the industrial conflicts of the Seventies were felt to be acts not of progress or desired change but of social stasis, followed by narrow election victories for one or other of the two main parties and ineffective leadership. I hadn't sat in the conference hall at Blackpool with the entranced Trevor as the Lady announced she was not for turning. Nor had I been out campaigning with the Scottish activists who were beginning to long for a similar kind of political straightforwardness. They were both demanding leadership based on distinctive policies that would not be discarded at the first sign of political opposition.

Nor was this simply a view held by clearly defined groups like Trevor's Conservatives and the Scottish Nationalists. As far as I could see it was a dominant mood of the mid-Seventies. It had its dangers, of course, this public yearning for strength and security above specific party political aspirations. And for a while those dangers had surfaced, foolishly and temporarily in Britain. This also was a definable part of politics in the Seventies. It was dispelled by the sheer force of Thatcherism with its revival of clear, ideologically based options. More clearly so, in my own life's experience, than ever before.

My Harold Wilson-induced political cynicism was now something like twenty years old and far too deeply rooted to be easily overthrown. From the election campaign of 1964, the only one I ever been to any extent emotionally involved in, I had carried troubled memories of gentle warnings by older friends and relatives that my enthusiasm was misguided. They had seen it all before, they assured me, and knew how little it actually meant. The promises of dynamic change were meaningless, even perhaps an illusion, especially when coming from a politician like Wilson who was not to be trusted. I had replied heatedly that they were wrong, that they didn't understand. I very quickly learned they were right, they had understood. There was no way I could shrug off those earlier experiences. Instead I had backed away from any kind of political involvement. But there must have been a certain amount of curiosity left lurking somewhere inside me, and I had Trevor to thank for stirring it up.

I was still far more interested in trying to complete my social history of the early modern English novel than in keeping up with the daily activities of politicians, but at least my eyes were now open. If there should be another incident like the one involving St John-Stevas it would be unlikely to pass me by. As before I continued to rely on late-night television news programmes to keep me informed, but this resource was now supplemented by one of my rare periodic spells of regular newspaper reading.

What I found there made me wonder whether Trevor really did know what he was talking about. England had moved swiftly into a political condition that bore many of the characteristics of civil war. It was on a fairly small scale at the moment but with all the potential for massive conflict. Inevitably so, Thatcher would have said, if she was to roll back the boundaries of socialism as she was promising to do. It was stirring stuff, but was any politician capable of undertaking such a task without becoming bogged down in the apathy that had for so long been characteristic of Britain? Was such action possible? A wonderful moment, as Trevor had recalled it, his eyes misty enough to suggest imminent tears. And so it may have been, but for now there was little sign of it bearing positive results. Far from it!

Already we had high inflation, collapsing industries, escalating unemployment, inner-city riots, and a Prime Minister and Chancellor of the Exchequer urging that these were necessary problems to be faced up to and overcome if the country was to move forward to a new era of freedom and prosperity. Even that might have made sense if unity and consistency were stolidly at work in shaping the process, but they weren't. There were daily attacks on government policies as misguided or plain wrong, not simply from the opposition but from people within the government itself. It was just as Trevor had warned. They were the politicians (the wets he had called them, using a word new to me) who had earlier claimed they were the victims of a gigantic bluff that would come to nothing. And they now seemed to be right as Thatcher herself and her most devoted ministers were shown to be bailing out the terminally sick British car industry and buying off the miners in a dispute over pit closures. If that wasn't turning back, what on earth was it?

This was the moment when Trevor decided to keep his last-minute promise to keep in touch, 'in one way or another.' It took the form of a plain postcard, inserted in an envelope, and addressed to me at the university. On one side of it, written neatly in forward-sloping capital letters were the words:

DON'T WORRY. IT WON'T HAPPEN AGAIN! T.

That was all. There was no attempt to explain why I wasn't to worry or to indicate what, among a variety of possible things, this particular 'it' might be referring to. Not that it was difficult, recalling Trevor's electioneering experiences, to guess at his meaning. I sat at the desk in my university office, to which at that time all mail was delivered by uniformed servitors at various points throughout the day, and read and reread the message, puzzled at first, then amused. It may have been vague on specifics, but the general purpose, the nature of the reassurance being offered, was obvious enough. The preparation was over, or perhaps was still being tidied up; token gestures had been made; sacrificial victims offered up; internal bluffs called. There was to be no more turning. Everything was straight ahead.

I was to receive similar postcards from Trevor at irregular intervals over the next four years. There were eleven in all: a fairly consistent batch of ten, and then, by itself, one floater. The messages were undated. No date was needed. The content usually fixed the moment of sending with some accuracy. As the cards came entirely from his side, with no communication or exchange of views between us, what was taking placed hardly qualified as any kind of correspondence. I did eventually send him one written reply, though that was little more than a friendly acknowledgement of the kind that asks for, and in fact received, no answer. In other words, I responded by not responding which is what Trevor himself had recommended.

All of the cards followed the original model in brevity and concision. They were allusive, sometimes cryptic, and written in the same eccentric manner. After the first of them Trevor modified the image of the knowledgeable insider he had established at our Bloomsbury tea party. I don't think this was a conscious decision on his part. It would have been forced upon him, a simple matter of facing up to reality. I assumed he was still working for the Conservatives at a constituency level and that he was as well up as ever on strategy and planning, but the political events now taking place around both of us, whether in Middlesex or Edinburgh, no longer required any specialist explanation. They were aggressively out in the open, there for everyone to experience. What could he tell me that wasn't in the public domain? Everything was all too immediate, too involving, to be upstaged or even matched by anything as shadowy as insider knowledge.

It was as though we had been caught, totally unprepared, in a violent mountain storm, with startling flashes of lightning out of a dry sky, swiftly followed by torrential rain and sweeping gales, all orchestrated by deafening peels of thunder from purple clouds. There was no more political lethargy, no wobble, no striving for a shaky consensus which had, anyway, been transformed into a very unfashionable political word. Everything was descending from an explosive centre. Being for or against meant being driven to adopt hitherto unprecedented public stances, a matter of take it or leave it. Inevitably the clash of opinions or forces was presented in terms of polarized ideologies, but that could now seem mere sophistry, a fearful hanging on to past attitudes and values in a conflict that soon became as one-sided as Trevor's postcards.

Some aspects of the old beliefs were still clung to, and nowhere more fiercely than in the universities, but far more was changing hands and palpably so, giving way to the violent natural force that Thatcherism appeared to have transformed itself into. It was unlike anything any of us had ever experienced before. But whether natural or unnatural and though still vague in definition, the ultimate effect promised to be definitive. Once the storm was over and had been replaced by some kind of calm, everyone seemed to understand that there could be no possibility of reverting to the way things once had been. Not in the foreseeable future there wasn't. It was the future that was being fought over. Never again would it be possible for British politicians to pretend nothing had happened, do a quick about turn, and stroll down the same old paths. At least, that was how it felt at the time.

And, for the most part Trevor's postcards reflected this mingled mood of excitement and astonishment. He was obviously thrilled that such events were unfolding and barely able to believe they were:

YES. REJOICE. JUST REJOICE. T.

This was a faithful repetition of Thatcher's gasp of relief at the news of South Georgia in the Falklands being recaptured by British troops. Until that moment it had still been possible for the war to go wrong. Now it looked certain that the Argentinean invasion would be repelled. Trevor was sharing the personal joy and the patriotic pride of his leader in the action taken on what she had presented as a vital issue for the country. And, of course, vital for her own career as well. If things had gone wrong she would probably have been finished, but they hadn't and her position was now stronger than before. Trevor's rejoicing would have covered this understanding as well as the news from the Falklands. I too was overwhelmed by the whole extraordinary episode, with the historian in me astonished that this flamboyant modern recreation of a classic and surely anachronistic colonial war had actually taken place. I could hardly believe it had happened.

Trevor, however, moved swiftly on. Once the danger point of South Georgia was overcome and the survival of his leader guaranteed, patriotism took over, a sense of pride that Britain was once again positively asserting itself in the world. This was made more than clear by his only other postcard that dealt with the war. He ignored the specific events leading to General Galtieri's overthrow, and saved his main feelings, of pride and bile in equal measure, for the Church of England:

MAY RUNCIE ROT IN HELL! T.

Here again, he was probably reflecting attitudes close to Thatcher's own, though if so she had shown unusual diplomatic tact in not making them public. The crime for which the Archbishop of Canterbury was to be eternally damned was his handling of a thanksgiving ceremony at St Paul's. Held supposedly to mark victory in the Falklands, Runcie had turned it into what many people, with Trevor very clearly among them, saw as a pacifist propaganda service that insulted the courageous actions of the British troops, alive as well and dead.

The Church of England's politically correct conscience mattered little to me. Nor did I much care whether Runcie's action was classifiable as mortal or venial. I had been astonished by Thatcher's bravado in forcing the issue through and full of admiration for the actions of the British servicemen in the Falklands. The politician could be safely left to speak for herself and her party, but the servicemen couldn't and to my mind their actions deserved more than a damagingly qualified form of public recognition. And they got it from Thatcher, defiantly so and in a form that could hardly have pleased Runcie. Nor, presumably, would he have approved of the highly partisan lasting memorial to the Falklands war, far removed from the pomp or pomposity of either Church or State, that I experienced and the memory of which I will always carry with me.

I joined with thousands of other people crowding the Forth Road Bridge to cheer the ships home from the south Atlantic as they passed directly underneath on their way to the Rosyth shipyard for refitting. Looked down upon in this way, they were tiny, frail, visibly scarred, stained by battle and hostile distant weather, neglected toy ships returning from a boisterous family outing on the local park pond before being taken home to receive a fresh coat of paint. Here, for a few passing moments, was a glimpse of reality, the job done, with the effusive tears and waving flags of emotional supporters, grieving relatives, neighbours, friends, lovers, strangers, Scots and English, all saying thank you without being herded together by the organ and choir of a church service or the inevitable point scoring of a parliamentary debate.

In comparison with the Falklands war, it was easy for me to anticipate Trevor's views on the miners' strike. Going to war had been a very different matter. Back in High Holborn that whole extraordinary event would have been considered a fantasy, a totally unpredictable political adventure. Where was the imagination fertile enough to invent the spontaneous, ramshackle, last-second planning that had sent a British task force off to the south Atlantic? Yet once the Falklands war had been replaced in the news by the miners' strike, Trevor was by no means alone in drawing close connections between them, making something inevitable, even fateful, about their similarities.

GALTIERI WITHOUT, SCARGILL WITHIN. T.

That was pointing up Thatcher's reiterated assertion that if Britain was ever to pull back from what by the mid-1970s had begun to look like unstoppable social and economic decline, then it must confront and defeat not simply the enemies without but the even more pernicious enemies within as well. These enemies were in one way or another classified as left wing, and it was part of the astonishing openness of Thatcher's public manner that she never hesitated to identify them. Or rather, who she thought they were which was not at all the same thing. Outside Britain the major enemy was state communism typified by the Soviet Union, while inside were all of the institutions, whether socialist, communist, or Marxist – the words tended to be used interchangeably – that still looked to the long-lost ideals of the Soviet Union for inspiration. Justification for action against any of these was voiced in ideological terms, though with little logic or consistency.

Curiously, Argentina was outside of Thatcher's normal parameters. It qualified for inclusion all right, being an anti-democratic military dictatorship, but by no stretch of the imagination could it be considered part of the Marxist or terrorist agencies that were supposedly set on undermining Britain. The military action against it was taken on quite other grounds. The IRA, in active operation throughout the period and responsible for killing several of Thatcher's closest supporters and narrowly failing to assassinate her as well, was certainly the most relentless of enemies within and a terrorist organization when viewed from the outside, but it was never Marxist. The other enemies within (Michael Foot's and then Neil Kinnock's Labour party, the BBC, certain national newspapers, Runcie's Church of England, the universities) hardly qualified as candidates at all but were cheerfully recruited when the mood fitted. There was no ambiguity, though, about the principal, and the most dangerous enemy within, excepting the IRA. It was the National Union of Miners led by Arthur Scargill. He fitted the bill to perfection; a self-confessed Marxist, an advocate of violence to achieve his desired political ends, someone who scorned the use of ballots, and dismissed the country's legally elected representatives as irrelevant to any cause he espoused.

Whether or not Trevor was right to equate the Falklands war and the miners' strike in the way he did, they were quickly swept up together within the thunderous atmosphere of unremitting conflict that Thatcherism generated. So was pretty well everything else. The apparent inevitability of it all was captured by *TINA. T.* This postcard threw me when I first received it. It was some time before I learned that it was an acronym for 'There is no alternative' a slogan much used by the Thatcher camp. It functioned as a kind of mnemonic both to reiterate the Lady's unturnability and to promote an image of her government as being in a state of non-stop unavoidable reformist activity.

In the spring of 1984, during the preliminary skirmishes before the miners' strike began, Trevor sent me a postcard that captured with some neatness the curiously similar motives and behaviour of both sides in the appalling events to come:

THE COMRADES ARE DELIRIOUSLY HAPPY. T.

The obvious comrades were Arthur Scargill and his supporters in the union. They were deliriously happy because they were getting the strike they wanted. But were Thatcher and the loyal members of her inner cabinet any less joyful? They had also waited a long time for this moment and were prepared for it, better prepared than the miners if I had understood Trevor correctly. It therefore made sense for him to be referring to both of the willing combatants and at the same time proclaiming his own confidence in the outcome of any conflict.

My feelings about the miners' strike were far more ambiguous. They were so intensely personal that it was virtually impossible for me to divorce them from the political issues involved. These were fairly straightforward and, I imagine, shared initially, whether openly or covertly, by most people, including politicians of all parties. This was particularly the case with the laws restricting trade union activity introduced in the early Eighties to deal with the kind of social disruption that had been influential in bringing the Thatcher government to power. The miners' strike itself was not even actively supported by other large unions. Few people of any kind would have approved the blatantly undemocratic and loudly proclaimed extra-parliamentary activities of Arthur Scargill who was happy to be seen ignoring both the government's reforms and the rights of his own union members to vote on strike action. It might seem that there could be no difficulty in me standing shoulder to shoulder with Trevor on this issue, but there was.

For as long as I could remember, coal miners had been held up to my family as models of working-class tenacity and goodness. They do, my father would tell us on every suitable occasion, 'a bloody filthy, dangerous job for all of us,' and there was never any cause for us to doubt the truth of his words. At the age of seven or eight, during the devastatingly cold winters of the late 1940s, I had regularly accompanied my older brother Harry, both of us wrapped up as well as we were able against the weather and often physically sick from the cold, doing what little I could do to help him push an adapted baby's pram to and from a local railway siding. We were collecting the rationed amounts of coal that were available to us in no other way, normal delivery and distribution having been cut or frozen out through shortages.

At home, a kitchen stove was the only form of heating we had, and the only source of hot water as well. On winter evenings, none of the family moved far from the kitchen until it was time for us to rush individually to our bitterly cold bedrooms. The kitchen fire was always alight, reduced in the summer but still necessary to provide hot water, a visible reminder of the immense debt all of us owed to the miners carrying out their 'bloody dangerous filthy jobs.' It is little exaggeration to say that in a family as poor as ours, the miners were often responsible for keeping us alive, or, at the very least, keeping us fit enough to allow us to survive. It was impossible in our family for there ever to be any resentment at whatever wages the miners received or demanded. 'They deserve every penny they get,' my father would have said. And that from a man who was obliged to work every hour open to him, knowingly undermining his health in the process, to earn enough to barely feed and house his wife and four children.

Unmoveable as that kind of solidarity may sound, it was essentially an emotional rather than a political response. My father paid his union dues and would have thought it morally wrong to vote for anyone other than the Labour Party. At the same time he was convinced that belonging to a union never brought him or his family any benefits whatsoever, all politicians of whatever party being 'in it for what they can get.' Nor would he have seen any contradiction between these attitudes. Not even his admiration for the miners could have persuaded him to consider going on strike, even if his union had thought it feasible to call one, which it was never in a position to do anyway. The main reason why his beliefs and actions could seem so contradictory was because every moment of his working life, which meant also of course the lives of his totally dependent wife and children, was spent so perilously close to the edge of disaster that it was impossible for him ever to think about confronting anything but the reality of the immediate moment.

Nor was this something applicable only to my father. It was rooted in social circumstances and conditions that even today are rarely understood by those people who set themselves up professionally to explain such matters in terms of a unified single entity called *the* working class. My father could happily confer heroic status on coal miners and at the same time reject the possibility of any worthwhile social change ever being achieved by concerted working-class action because he understood that the links supposedly binding us and the miners together were largely illusory. What made us working class was not so much my father's job as our economic conditions. We belonged to the vast, diffuse mass of the urban poor; London in our case, but duplicated in every large city throughout Britain and applicable to many rural communities as well. Solidarity with other people in similar circumstances to us was not underpinned by any kind of group identity other than the constant struggle to avoid being permanently trapped by abject poverty. It was often notoriously difficult to define in terms of jobs done or money earned who was or was not working class. Or even, who thought of themselves as being working class or didn't, because in our world that could vary enormously.

In contrast, the miners were distinct communities – topographically, socially, and politically. They were also in control of a crucial energy source. This kind of power was held by other highly unionized industrial and manufacturing workers. Although hardly anyone would have believed it at the time, in the early Eighties most of these groups of workers were on their way out, virtually finished as effective organizations capable of significantly influencing or even overthrowing elected governments. The nearest equivalents in London were the dockers and print workers. Many families like mine had connections with them but the exclusivity of their unions still kept them to a certain extent separate from the wider urban working-class community. They were also both on their way out: the dockers before Thatcher put in an appearance, the printers very much under pressure from her. Within the next twenty or thirty years, the working-class structures into which I had been born and which had conditioned my childhood and youth would be reversed. Miners, dockers, printers, steel workers, boilermakers, dockers, car workers and the rest, with all their power, grime, and conflict, would follow the nineteenth-century mill and factory workers and be transformed beyond recognition. With a few nationwide exceptions like transport workers, they were replaced, in terms of mass working-class numbers, by millions of semi-skilled, indifferently educated workers in the service industries.

The miners' strike has come to be seen as a key event in this larger process, but it was far from instrumental in bringing it about. At the time it was even difficult to understand why it was taking place at all, apart, of course, from Scargill's determination that it should. Otherwise the strike appeared to be without any kind of definite focus. It was centrally against the closure of mines but wanted nothing to do with changing work patterns or bringing the industry more in line with modern practices. Nor was it directly concerned with making working conditions healthier or safer, or securing a better future for miners, or ensuring that the loss-making industry should become less of a burden to tax-payers. If anything, it seemed to be against such changes. It wasn't even about earning more money or, indeed, any working-class aspirations that would have been recognized in my family. As far as it was possible to make sense of what was going on, the striking miners, who constituted anyway by no means a clear majority, wanted nothing to change. If possible they wanted to go backwards, to do everything possible to retain their 'bloody dangerous filthy jobs' in much the same unchanging bloody, dangerous filthy conditions.

For my mother and father there was a pride in their working-class status that could only have been fully expressed if backed by the kind of solidarity with others that they didn't have. In fact, it was probably our own lack of organization that made us believe that political or strike action taken by more organized groups was on our behalf as well as theirs. Not that any benefits gained through such strikes usually extended to us, except once again at an emotional level, a victory worthily achieved. None of this would have been regarded as in any sense inconsistent with an equal determination by my parents that their children should not have to endure the same kinds of poverty and degradation they had suffered. If anyone had tried to tell my mother especially that she should be happy to keep her children within the kind of working-class environment they had grown up in she would have told them scornfully that they didn't know what they were talking about. Her mission in life, the mission for which she willingly gave *her* life, was to ensure that her children moved on to better things, and to her that meant education and ceasing to be working class, or poor which was actually the more appropriate term.

For us, and for millions of others in much the same situation, class identity was not defined by a local or developed community which we could boast of belonging to, as it was so powerfully for the miners and other similarly based industrial workers. It was, surely, this image of communities under threat that, regardless of the rightness or wrongness of the case at issue, brought widespread public sympathy for the miners and disgust at Thatcher's part in the conflict. For the diffused and otherwise unconnected masses of the poor and deprived there was no remotely comparable form of solidarity. As I have said, I have never found much understanding among outsiders of just how different these types of working-class experience can be. There is, though, at least one great English writer who has placed at the centre of his work the ambiguities of belonging and not belonging to working-class life, the competing attractions of staying and leaving, that I grew up with. That is D H Lawrence and, curiously enough, he came not from the struggling mass of urban poor but from a long-established coal-mining community.

Once the miners' strike was over and Thatcher's victory uneasily granted, there was no relaxation, no let up, no change of pace. The relentless pattern of overthrow and upheaval continued as before, though occurring now within a very different atmosphere. The economy was visibly improving. People were better off, and knew it. Gone were the debilitating levels of inflation and demeaning IMF bailouts of the 1970s. Coincidentally, and of massive significance, was the rapid growth throughout the 1980s at both home and work of modern technology. Although owing nothing immediately to the government, it combined effortlessly with the financial and social aspirations of Thatcherism. Individual prosperity was now being actively targeted in unprecedented ways. It was suddenly good to earn, have, keep, and spend money, with individual effort being encouraged by tax cuts, house and share ownership, and politically engineered financial windfalls.

POWER TO THE PEOPLE, NOT TO THE STATE. T.

Trevor hadn't been so gleeful since the liberation of South Georgia. This time he was celebrating the victory of 'popular capitalism' as it soon came to be called. No doubt he had specifically in mind the privatization of nationalized industries, the clearest evidence yet of a real shift of power from the State to the People and brought about by the dismantling of a key post-war principle of socialist Britain. Thought of until now as inviolable, it too was suddenly gone, replaced, in theory at least, by an old-style individualism that urged people to rely less on the State and to take control of their own lives and finances. Of course, there were many people who couldn't do anything of the sort, but there were a surprisingly large number who could, and wanted to.

I was particularly interested in a different aspect of this shift of power from the State to the People, rather more so I suspect than Trevor. Beyond the privatization of specific state-owned industries in Britain, Thatcher's attack was increasingly focused on the very heart of world-wide state Socialism, calling for it to discard its totalitarian control and to return power to the people. There was something of a conjurer's sleight of hand about her position on this because without active American support, made real by the friendship Thatcher forged with President Reagan, she would have looked ridiculous, claiming an influence for Britain in the world that it clearly didn't have. But firm American backing allowed her anti-Soviet stance to came over as audacious rather than foolish. That Britain itself was in the middle of a financial revolution, fomented in large part by frenetic denationalization, gave her a rather lopsided right to advise other countries to follow suit and set about dismantling the repressive state power that governed their lives.

When she had been dubbed 'the iron lady' by the Soviet Union she had still to do anything substantial to deserve the label. Now she was making up to Mikhail Gorbachev in a very public manner long before he became the General Secretary of the Soviet Union, inviting him to Britain for face-to-face talks, and starting her series of personal visits to countries behind the Iron Curtain where she openly promoted Western values. Her visit to the Soviet Union she treated as though it was a British election campaign, turning a television appearance into an unprecedented live debate, taking a regal walkabout among the inhabitants of a Moscow housing estate, busily lecturing them on the political rights and wrongs of the situation they were in and what they should be doing about it. She was greeted with genuine enthusiasm, not only as a prophet and a radical, but also as a glamorous, fashionably dressed representative of capitalism. With no irony whatsoever, though it was inevitably noted as such by British commentators, she became an ardent supporter of Polish Solidarity, calling for the formation of free trade unions there and in other Soviet satellites, and was hugely praised by those whose aspirations she was supporting. The louder she spoke (or shouted) the more admired she became abroad, and the more her influence shrank at home.

While all of this was swirling around, creating new storms in the already tempestuous British political atmosphere, Trevor seemed to have fallen silent. There was something like a year's gap in the postcards. The period of grace he had spoken of as being available to him to help see through the remaining college diploma courses should have passed by now. I had no way of knowing what he might be doing and was particularly pleased by the arrival of a new postcard. Seeing once again the familiar envelope brought home to me how much I had enjoyed this curiously intimate form of communication that I was beginning to think was probably over.

The postcard inside the envelope didn't do much to clarify that situation. Nor did it pick up on where the earlier postcards had left off a year earlier. Instead, it provoked in me a new kind of concern. Although still in the business of keeping me informed about the current state of politics, Trevor's manner, his *literary* manner had changed. Not in any obvious way. It was simply that the old jauntiness came over as a trifle strained, the former ingenuity not quite there any longer:

TARZAN NO MATCH FOR JANE. T.

Tarzan was the affectionate nickname that the Tory rank and file had long attached to Michael Heseltine to describe his barnstorming performances at party conferences. Jane of course was Tarzan's jungle mate, in this case transformed into Margaret Thatcher. Heseltine was currently the Minister of Defence and a supporter of Thatcher's anti-Soviet military alliance with Ronald Reagan. He was also fiercely ambitious, a conscious, manipulative populist in a way that the more intuitive Thatcher never was or needed to be, and unashamedly set on using his tree-swinging popularism to replace her as leader of the Party. The newspapers were currently preoccupied with what looked like his latest attempt to supplant Thatcher by means of a curiously open *coup d'état*, a move I had been inclined to dismiss out of hand as doomed to failure. For the first time, one of Trevor's postcards gave me a jolt.

It wasn't clear from the card whether it had been written when Heseltine was still to make the well publicized exit from the cabinet that led directly to his resignation or whether it had been written during the build-up to those events. I think it must have been the latter. Not that it mattered very much. Trevor's main purpose was clearly to make it known that his own loyalty was unchanged, that Thatcher/Jane was perfectly capable of seeing off this particular pretender to her treetop throne. As, indeed, she did turn out to be. But the challenge itself revealed that in some respects her position as leader was unexpectedly weak. She even had to face what amounted to a vote of no confidence in the Commons. The papers were full of her unpopularity in and out of parliament, and it was this I suppose that seemed to undermine the jollity of Trevor's jungle language. Was he worried, less assured than previously? It felt like it to me.

The postcard which followed quickly on from the Tarzan message continued to leave all these conjectures unanswered, although it did finally settle what Trevor was up to. It was my longest ever communication from him, filling one side of the postcard and moving on to the reverse. It was almost long enough to qualify as a letter, and a literary one at that:

> *CAN'T HOLD ON ANY LONGER.*
> *OFF TO JOIN THE YUPPIES.*
> *THE VICTIM OF A REVOLUTIONARY OUTRAGE.*
> *KEEP UP THE GOOD WORK.*
> *ALL BEST WISHES. T.*

This message I had no trouble in understanding. Whatever his dealings with the polytechnic it was now plain that he was about to give up teaching entirely. It was less certain whether the same was true of his political activities. For the moment he had taken a job in the City of London. I was surprised but only briefly. I should have been able from the beginning to identify him in this way, and I most certainly don't mean as a yuppy! That was just one of the many jokes in his packed message. It was a businessman he had looked like. Or at least what I imagine an off-duty businessman might then have looked look like. Everything about him had said there was money in the background, stashed away waiting for him to do something about it. I even suddenly recalled the words he had muttered to himself when telling me about being forced to move from his college: 'Still it might never happen…it doesn't have to.'

Now, he was taking up that other option, less personally attractive to him but one that had always been there. Perhaps he was reverting to type, perhaps simply claiming a place for himself within yet another area of British society that had changed beyond recognition in the past few years. It was at least certain that he wouldn't be conforming to the yuppy phenomenon. This was something I did know about from personal experience. For some months past, along with academics all over the country, I had been busily writing references to help many of our most highly qualified graduates to head south and join the gold rush.

They, not Trevor, were the yuppies, models of upward mobility. Like Oscar Wilde's Bunbury, Trevor had been exploded. He was the victim of a revolutionary outrage, except that this revolution was of a very modern variety, with the bomb being set off not by heavily cloaked nihilists, as Lady Bracknell would have assumed, but by the financial Big Bang. We're the Radicals now, Thatcher had come to enjoy announcing, and how correct she was. Beside her, current parliamentary socialists and university Marxists were looking paler and more ineffectual than ever.

I knew this was one postcard which had to be answered and I spent some time wondering how I should do it. At first I thought of an affectionate imitation of Trevor's own style and manner, but decided that that carried too large a risk of getting the tone wrong. Moving quite a bit the other direction, I considered sending a few typewritten lines on university notepaper. That idea I gave up as well and went instead for a touristy approach. I looked for a characteristic pictorial postcard of Edinburgh and settled on a windy, rainswept view of the Meadows with Arthur's Seat showing indistinctly in the background. I wrote Edinburgh at the top of the blank side, added the date, began Dear Trevor, thanked him for his postcards which I had greatly valued, wished him the very best of luck in his new career, and signed it Peter. I sealed the card in an envelope and sent it to Trevor's former college, adding a note on the envelope asking for it to be forwarded to him if necessary. After I had dropped it into a post box I found myself worrying whether I had taken too much for granted. Was I right to assume so certainly that this had been Trevor's way of announcing the end of our one-sided relationship?

As things turned out, it was, or very nearly so.

* * * *

It was inevitable that the relationship between universities and the Thatcher government would be stormy. There were a few nationally established academics who came out publicly to support the political and economic changes taking place, but probably more who kept their approval diplomatically to themselves. That really had to be the case. After all, Thatcher's own success as a politician may have been largely a matter of gut instinct, but the policies now being pursued so aggressively and on so many different levels had had a more considered intellectual gestation than those of any government since that of 1945.

In Edinburgh, the vast majority of town and gown, with little else necessarily in common, were at one in refusing to have anything at all to do with Mrs Thatcher. Many refused even to hear her name spoken in their company, let alone seriously consider any of her policies. They would clamp their lips, cover their ears or turn their backs and retreat for safety behind the alternative political policies that were being so publicly derided and flayed. Students, whether Scots or English, clung for salvation to their usual vaguely defined left-wing tenets. For the moment, support for the Scottish Nationalists had yet to recover from the defeat they had suffered along with James Callaghan's Labour government in the general election of 1979. There was, though, one curious and potentially significant act of Scottish intent in 1982 when the constituency of Glasgow Hillhead discarded its traditional Conservative affiliation and voted for Roy Jenkins, the leader of the recently formed SDP. Although the result in itself was never regarded as much more than a vague gesture of discontent, in retrospect it can be taken as an early indication of things to come, with the Conservative Party on its way to being all but permanently banished from Scotland in favour of first the Labour Party and then the SNP.

On behalf of British universities, Oxford stepped forward to adopt a similar kind of symbolic role to that of Glasgow Hillhead by announcing its intention of withholding from Thatcher the honorary degree it usually conferred on British prime ministers. The reason given was the damage being done to higher education by the public spending cuts she had imposed shortly after her government took office. The public snub was greeted ecstatically in Edinburgh. This was the way to show the dreadful woman that the universities at least were not going to bow down before her and her mindless monetarism. Trevor, though, had regarded it as an opportunity to exercise a spot of unfamiliar sarcasm:

WELL, THAT'S IT THEN.

WHAT WILL WE DO WITHOUT OXFORD? T.

What indeed! Or rather, as of course he really meant, what would Oxford do without us? Oxford may have been in proud possession of centuries of tradition and endowments, but nowadays it was essentially no different from any other British university in being, down to the newest of the new and the poorest of the poor, heavily dependent for its survival on government money. There wasn't much endowed wealth apparent in Edinburgh, but we shared with Oxford a pride in ancient traditions, small group teaching, and lofty educational prestige. We also had different and longer degree courses than those in England. Scotland even boasted that it was better at higher education than the rest of Britain. Whether or not, the cost of it was still being met almost entirely by British taxpayers.

Earlier in the century these financial matters had been handled in a less centralized manner and on behalf of a tiny proportion of the population. Before the 1939-45 war a university education was not generally regarded as essential for anyone building a career or even for entrance into the established professions. All of this had changed drastically by the time Oxford was thumbing its nose at the current prime minister. The university world was not only different from before the war, it was becoming barely recognizable from the one I had entered as a mature student just twenty years earlier. By the start of the 1980s universities were in serious trouble and for reasons that had little to do fundamentally with the government's recent financial cuts. Higher education was expanding, but the universities themselves were no longer growing or developing in any significant way. In fact they were having to regularly trim their ambitions and teaching methods. Nor did they show much willingness to examine what was going wrong. In Edinburgh, the blind hatred of everything to do with Thatcherism led to the most extraordinary atmosphere of ignorance and denial. Left-wing attitudes tended to be based on, or justified by, the usual fantasies about working-class life. This resulted in a series of spectacularly wrong political predictions.

In 1979 I was assured with confidence by virtually everyone about me that the working classes would never vote for Thatcher in this or any other election. She went on to lead the Conservatives in three elections and won them all with large majorities, something that could never have been achieved without strong working-class support. Working-class women especially, I was told mockingly, wouldn't vote for her because her snooty personal image was an affront to them. I enjoyed the private memory of my paternal grandmother more than twenty years earlier saying to me one lunchtime: 'Well, I tell you what, Pete, here's one person who's never had it so good.' She then went to her local for her daily glass of Guinness before walking on to the polling booth to turn her back on Labour and vote Conservative for the very first time. She was helping to return to power a prime minister whose public image was so far removed from the working classes that he made Mrs Thatcher look like the charwoman my grandmother had been for most of her life. Equally certain odds were placed on the impossibility of the working classes supporting a blatantly imperialist war; wanting to buy the council houses they lived in; agreeing with the policy of denationalization or welcoming the chance to own shares in newly privatized companies. It was also confidently asserted that there would be no working-class support for legislation to curb union power, the upgrading of Britain's nuclear forces or any other kind of military defence; or the calls on the Soviet Union to liberate its imprisoned satellites, one of which, the GDR, was even frequently promoted by left wingers as the kind of social and political model Britain should be following.

The same policy of non-cooperation was applied to university education itself. Nothing was to change because no change was needed. It was assumed there should be a continuous expansion of the student population; universities, as autonomous institutions, were to retain total responsibility for running themselves; academic staff must continue to hold life tenure regardless of their individual ability or competence; students were to continue to be provided with free education; and the ever-increasing cost of higher education was to be borne by the government/taxpayer. How could students or universities be expected to contribute anything? They weren't concerned with the squalid business of making money, only with spending it.

In Leicester, as the Sixties drew to a close, I had observed with some fascination the rapidly changing nature of the academic world I had recently been accepted into. Puzzled as well. As I have described in 'Monica,' I was a new boy then with no experience of how things had once been and every reason to accept things as they now were. It felt perfectly natural for me to watch handsome new university buildings growing from nothing (as at Sussex) or replacing rickety temporary structures (as at Leicester). I was also fully at ease with the burgeoning student populations at both of these universities.

And for a while (a very short while as it turned out) most other involved people shared my mood of acceptance. It did, after all, carry a highly reputable semi-official blessing in the form of the report by Lord Robbins on higher education in Britain. Robbins hadn't been responsible for the founding of the new universities, but his report was contemporaneous with their opening and came to be seen, quite reasonably, as part of the same effortless procession into a glorious future for higher education. What was on offer was the transformation of Britain from a country where a very small minority of young people went to university into a country where every young person capable of benefiting from a place at University was to be provided with one. The report was published in 1963, accepted enthusiastically at the very last minute by the outgoing Conservative government under Sir Alec Douglas-Home and picked up eagerly by Harold Wilson's incoming Labour government. It marked a rare moment of cross-party unity, and was to prove a liability for every subsequent government down to the present day, whether Labour or Conservative.

All seemed well at first because an exceptionally large sum of government money was pledged to start implementing the report's main proposals. Throughout the mid-Sixties I never remember being aware of any felt discrepancy among students or staff between what we all were and what we could expect to go on being. But then, I belonged to a truly fortunate generation of university students. Nor would there be in the near future any reason for younger students to feel otherwise. Even when I moved to Leicester a few years later I had no sense that this kind of confident optimism wasn't entirely reasonable, though my change from student to teacher was still unsettling, and not only for the personal reasons explored in 'Monica.'

Viewed from the inside, all of the growth, the new buildings going up and the expanding student numbers seemed matters of curiously little importance. Not because we undervalued them, but because they were never questioned. We even hardly noticed or commented on the fact that as the Sixties faded away so did the number of new buildings and student numbers. They were phenomena to be accepted rather than experienced, taken for granted, never thought about. We just sat and waited for things to happen. During departmental meetings, whenever a question arose concerning an issue of substantial planning, or even relatively small matters such as financing a new course or facilities, there was bound to arise from one or other of my senior colleagues a mournful bee-like buzzing that came over to me phonetically as *Ewegeesee, Ewegeesee, Ewegeesee.* Being invoked by this despairing mantra was what I eventually came to recognize as UGC (the University Grants Committee), the organization responsible for distributing government grants to universities every five years. The very thought of this 'Quinquennial' distribution, as it was known, created jitters throughout the university, and it mattered little whether it was near the start or end of the five year cycle, whether the worry was about how much we should ask for or how much we would be given. Once negotiations had taken place and grants allotted, individual universities became responsible for how the money was to be spent. The constant agitation and uncertainty about the Quinquennial distribution indicated that something was seriously wrong with the whole procedure. What was taking place, though we didn't think of it in these terms at the time, was the unravelling of Utopia.

The UGC was in an impossible situation, not least because of its own working assumptions that, regardless of any expansion or growth, the autonomous nature of universities and the cost of student education should remain essentially unchanged. There was in fact little it could do to justify that position. Its task was to distribute money to universities to keep them going and to fund approved projects. But the UGC had no money of its own, and the universities had very little. The size of the grants the UGC distributed were determined entirely by what it received from the government, and because university autonomy was regarded as a sacred concept, the government was in effect expected to have no say in how the money that it alone provided was to be spent.

There was only one way the recommendations of the Robbins report could be implemented, and that was by means of a permanent blank cheque. This was something that no government of whatever political persuasion was able or willing to countenance. It was also becoming worryingly apparent that higher education was by no means only a matter of allotting university places. There were all sorts of other colleges and educational institutions to be taken take into account. They were essentially vocational and treated as inherently inferior to universities. Yet large numbers of university students were also studying specialist subjects that would lead to clearly defined jobs after graduation. What made them so different? This might not have mattered so much if the universities could also have proudly displayed the increased number of students in science and technology called for by Robbins. But they couldn't. The majority of university students were still taking predominantly arts-based courses with no specific employment in view. The scientists whose arrival had been eagerly anticipated were slow to appear. But they were certainly needed if a new Britain was going to be 'forged in the white heat' of the technological revolution that Harold Wilson had grandly promised shortly before he came to power in 1964. As the unsolved problems accumulated, they were, anyway, rendered largely irrelevant by the hyperinflation of the Seventies which wiped away the slightest possibility that university funding could be maintained at anything like its former level.

Nor, after the mid-Sixties, did any government even pretend to advocate policies consistent with Robbins. Government legislation, disparate but relentlessly regular, forced universities again and again to confront financial difficulties they hadn't anticipated and were incapable of dealing with by themselves. The UGC struggled to help, but was itself limited by the same problems. One of the biggest shocks for universities was the realization that the UGC grants they received were expected to cover only the salaries and general cost of academics. The cost of appointing and paying the growing number of non-academics – from administrators and skilled laboratory technicians through to servitors and cleaners – was not intended to be met from the same source. No wonder one of the things that had most struck me at Leicester, as it filtered down to departmental level, was the fraught issue (and the angry divisions it provoked) of administrative responsibilities being thrust more and more onto academics.

Government insistence on cutbacks and constitutional changes were made easier to introduce by a sharp decline in sympathy, among politicians and public alike, for the privileged status enjoyed by universities after several years of campus riots and sit-ins, with visiting politicians trying to explain the need for change being met by screaming, spitting, paint-throwing, state-funded, left-wing students. Only three years after Harold Wilson had set aside the money needed to fund Robbins, his education secretary was creating in modern polytechnics a new kind of higher education that would be cheaper to run (not least because the cost at first was to be shared with local authorities), absorb many of the miscellaneous colleges, and be primarily vocational in its teaching. A conscious, openly acknowledged reason for establishing this second tier of higher education was that it would help to maintain the privileged and unchanged status of universities. It actually had the opposite effect.

Polytechnics were a great success in all sorts of ways with both politicians and aspiring students who were now competing for limited university places. Within a few years there were more polytechnics than universities in Britain and more students studying in them. It wouldn't be long before politicians gleefully realized that far from being allowed to struggle along as poor relatives of higher education, the polytechnics themselves could be metamorphosed into universities, thus solving any problems about the expansion of student numbers and, in the process, settling all sorts of other problems handed down from Robbins. The drive was no longer to urge polytechnics to aspire to academic standards set by universities, but for universities to become more like polytechnics.

Although the universities stayed up there shouting defiance and urging the UGC to squeeze more and more money from the government, they must have known that their bluff had been called. There were some signs that given the right guidance universities might be willing to try to do something for themselves. This was made lucidly apparent by the vexed question of fees paid by foreign students. A portion of the amount received had long been an alternative source of income for universities. It was only small and varied greatly according to the attractiveness of an individual university's academic reputation and topographical location: obviously good for, say, Cambridge or Edinburgh, but not so good for many other places. When, after years of vacillation, the government ruled that universities could henceforth charge foreign students for the full cost of their fees, there was a rush to take maximum advantage of this new source of cash. University departments suddenly found themselves competing not only among themselves, but also with the advertising and tourist industries by designing posters and fliers to promote the advantages they could offer to students from overseas. It also led to lively squabbles over who exactly within the universities should receive the cash. All of this led to the emergence of new and unexpected talents among academics. It also forced universities to make long overdue assessments of just what kind of education they were actually offering and what, in money terms, it was worth.

The impact on overall funding of this activity was relatively slight, but the point had got across that money wasn't something that came only from the government. It was a valuable lesson and in Edinburgh where some of us had enjoyed our forays into advertising and tourism, there was an adventurous attempt to give it a wider application. Without making extravagant claims for what took place, it could nonetheless be reasonably described as something of a revolution. Small, but sensible and home grown, fermented, planned and successfully executed intramurally, it was carried triumphantly through against what I personally had considered were insurmountable odds.

Fergusson Murray, the much admired Scottish poet and scholar, had always had something of a maverick reputation. In academic terms that is. For a start he didn't belong properly to a particular department. He never had. He was one of those relatively unusual people who are recruited into universities when they are fairly advanced in years as a way of acknowledging their distinguished achievements outside. This had been done by appointing him to a Readership in Scottish Archaeology which was not a department in its own right, though he was happily welcomed by Archaeology itself which was. He was also made a professor of Scottish literature. This again was honorary because at that time the university didn't have a department of Scottish literature for him to be a professor of, and he tended to lead a wandering part-time existence between English language and English literature. None of this uncertainty about where exactly he belonged came from insensitivity on the part of the university. It was actually a sign of Murray's genuine originality. Honours were being heaped upon him. He had recently retired from his various honorary university posts, been awarded emeritus status by the Archaeology department, and was the recipient of an Anglo-American *festschrift* that celebrated a remarkable career, notably his three volumes of Gaelic poems, his discovery of an unexpectedly large number of Pictish survivals and his imaginative recreation of the murderous tribal relations between Picts and Scots. The honours he was receiving were all well deserved but some of his admirers felt he should receive a more public form of recognition. They elected to hold a large international conference in his honour and formed an interdepartmental committee to establish how this could best be done.

Whether there is much point in many of the conferences universities hold is open to doubt, but they are popular with the participants, although not always or necessarily it has to be said for scholarly reasons. But, popular they are. They are usually organized by individual departments and are expensive to set up, with travel, accommodation, academic sideshows, and local publicity for visitors all needing to be paid for somehow or other. It's that 'somehow or other' that reveals the ingenuity that universities are most certainly capable of displaying if driven to it. What happens is that individual departments and faculties make available the special funds they have all set aside for travel and research. They also often provide, free or at cost, various other facilities. Everybody chips in. Fees are paid by outside participants, and costs are spread thinly and broadly. As a result, departments that wouldn't normally be in a position to bear the whole cost of a large conference don't need to.

The committee set up to honour Fergusson Murray assumed that this system would work for them, but it ran into trouble. Archaeology, keen to act as host, was too small to distribute individual conference grants in the usual way. It therefore asked the university to help directly with funding on the grounds that Murray's outstanding distinction was a credit to the entire academic community, in and beyond Scotland. The request was acknowledged as just and fair but simply not possible to grant. Not only would it be storing up trouble to set such a precedent, but the despicable pressures being exerted daily by the Thatcher government made anything but bare financial survival impossible for the university to consider.

The only alternative the committee could come up with was a cut-price weekend conference. This it was felt would have been insulting to Murray and therefore worse than nothing. And for a while nothing was what it looked like being. Plans on how to ditch the conference in the most tactful manner were underway when a possible solution was proposed by a member of the committee. He was an American, a visiting professor in the department of Economics, an archaeology enthusiast, a personal friend of Murray's and one of the co-editors of the *festschrift*. Quietly and politely he told the committee they were making a huge amount of unnecessary fuss. Why bother with the university at all? Sponsorship was the answer. There must be dozens of Scottish firms based in Edinburgh who would be only too willing to come up with a measly few thousand pounds in return for some worldwide niche publicity. What the visiting American thought to be a matter of common sense caused outrage.

I wasn't personally a member of the committee, but I had a friend who was. We shared a number of rather unfashionable historical interests and would often meet together for lunch in the University Staff Club. From him I gained some intriguing insights into what was going on behind the scenes. Several members of the committee regarded the sponsorship suggestion as contemptible and rejected it out of hand. Universities were above such things, set apart, beyond commercial practices, and quite rightly so. Others, on a similar line, retreated for safety into outraged facetiousness, a much used academic form of snobbish humour. Who, they asked, were these Scottish sponsors who would be willing to become involved in such serious activities? Kilt manufacturers, perhaps? A whisky distiller? How about a local butcher whose adverts for a very popular haggis were carried throughout Edinburgh on the sides of buses? Would these now be replaced by adverts showing kilted archaeologists, contentedly at their work in the Highlands, pausing only to refresh themselves with a swig of whisky and a forkful of haggis?

The provoker of these degrading possibilities kept calm. He said he could see nothing wrong with the products mentioned which were to his mind characteristically and respectably Scottish. In fact, they were very much in line with what he thought might work perfectly well. But it was actually shortbread he was thinking of. At the moment it was just an idea and he offered to think it out more fully and report back to the next meeting. He was given reluctant permission to do so, but on condition that in the meantime other members of the committee could be allowed to sound out Professor Murray on the question of his Pictish studies being sold over the counter with packets of shortbread. After all, it was his reputation that was at stake, and as he would almost certainly want to have nothing to do with the plan that would be the end of it.

Over lunch a couple of weeks later I heard that the crucial committee meeting had passed in a state of dreamy bliss, for its supporters anyway. It was announced that a small Edinburgh manufacturer of shortbread called McCornish would be honoured to act as sponsors. They were willing immediately to put down five thousand pounds and to meet any costs involved in publicity, the nature of which they promised to discuss in advance with the committee, and to consider further limited financial donations in order to make this the dignified occasion it deserved to be. The doubters were finally put to rest by a letter from Professor Murray. Far from feeling tainted by commercialism, the great man showed himself to be fully up on the latest financial trends. He said he would be delighted if the conference could go ahead without a penny of public money being spent on it, and would himself take whatever role in the proceedings the committee thought appropriate. He also added a postscript saying that he was especially fond of shortbread and had always liked to carry some with him on digs.

Two members of the committee resigned, but the rest embraced the new opportunities. The conference went ahead much as normal with individual participants, British and foreign, applying for their customary grants in the customary manner where these were available. The McCornish funds were used to meet any imbalance and to pay for receptions and keynote lectures. They also covered the cost of a closing public forum featuring Professor Murray that was thrown open to anyone, town and gown, who wished to attend. On all sides they responded to the whole affair with tact and imagination and no doubt also made a healthy profit from the publicity.

To meet the grandeur of the occasion they had designed a special, extremely elegant new box, olive green in colour with gold trimmings, to contain the shortbread. They used the same colours for the single free-standing poster that was placed discreetly at the corner of every stage where a lecture was taking place. At receptions, platters of shortbread were passed round with the wine (both paid for by McCornish). When the hugely successful conference closed, each delegate – a total of just over fourteen hundred – was presented with a special gift-wrapped box of McCornish 'Conference' shortbread.

* * * *

There was no chance that the larger problems in which universities were now engulfed were going to be settled in quite this fairytale manner. Some universities were already beginning to cooperate experimentally with commerce and industry, but, like the fees from overseas students, these weren't going to amount to any kind of comprehensive solution. Things were far too bad for that. All that could be done was to gather together the growing backlog of neglected university business, temporarily patch it up, take it out of the hands of the UGC and hand it over to the government for a solution to be imposed. The hostile atmosphere between universities and government remained, though leavened slightly for one of the sides by an element of something very like relief. For just as the Robbins report had been launched in a rare moment of political cooperation, so it was now closed down with both of the main political parties seeming to be in tacit agreement with each other. The reforms, or more properly the rationalizing of changes that had been long underway, were initiated during the final years of the Thatcher government, continued by her successor John Major, and pushed on vigorously by Tony Blair's New Labour Party.

From beginning to end, Robbins's dream of what university education in Britain might become had lasted for little more than a quarter of a century. By the close of that period very few of the principles, teaching practices, or special educational and financial benefits for staff or students which Robbins had inherited and aimed to develop further, stayed in force. In any circumstances this slow demolition of what had once been an inspiring educational ideal would have been a melancholy experience. But because the late Eighties and early Nineties were so full of uncertainty and confusion, and so remarkable for all kinds of collapsing structures, the universities no longer seemed a special case and the early stages of their final decline took place as though by accident, piecemeal, haphazardly. Although the entire process is often attributed to the reformist zeal of Thatcher, she played a relatively small part in the unravelling of Britain's university dream. Indeed, before the final transformation began in earnest, she herself had been destroyed.

The growing instability that Trevor's Tarzan postcard seemed to disclose had been pushed quickly into the open for everyone to see. There was, though, no slow downgrading of political activity. That was never Thatcher's way. Ignoring public disagreements between members of the cabinet, open challenges to her authority, and growing discontent among backbenchers, she continued as though nothing untoward was happening. She even led her party to victory and another impressive Commons majority in a third general election. But things weren't the same, and the air of seeming to carry on as normal was illusory.

The tone that had always been dictatorial but compelling enough to persuade voters and politicians to follow policies that only a decade earlier would have been unthinkable to many of them, was now harsh, strident, and unconvincing. New policies, not in essence greatly different from those of earlier days, no longer felt necessary or essential. Nor did they seem justifiable any longer in terms of the eternal battle between good and evil that featured so centrally in Thatcher's political vocabulary. Moral boundaries were becoming blurred, actions regarded as arbitrary or unfair. It was easy enough to see 'Red' Ken Livingstone as another version of Red Arthur Scargill, but the abolition of the London County Council, Livingstone's fiefdom, came over as an act of personal spite rather than a crucial blow struck in the name of British democracy. The long awaited reform of the local ratings system in the form of the ridiculous Poll Tax was even more pernicious. Wanted by no one, morally and socially unjustifiable, it looked exactly what it must surely have been, an act motivated by blind obstinacy. Plans to take it apart it were being discussed even before Thatcher was forced out of office by her cabinet colleagues.

Beginning in the autumn of 1989 my general habit of watching late-night television news became a compulsion as the Berlin wall was literally chipped away and the inhabitants of the GDR, followed by other iron-curtain countries, simply walked into the West. At the end, it all appeared so easy, so obvious. It was an event that could be seen as epitomizing everything Thatcher had worked for and at the same time something she had never believed she would live to see. Even Ronald Reagan may have been taken by surprise. But at least he was on hand to cheer it on, while Mrs Thatcher, so full of openly expressed hatred and distrust of Germany and European unity was left wishing it hadn't happened. The effective ending of the Cold War, one of the major turning points in modern world history, should have meant so much to her. It was certainly something she could rightly claim to have played an active part in helping to bring about.

Nor was that all. She might have welcomed these events in more than simply European terms. For here was the collapse of the very model held up for admiration and emulation by all those left-wing enemies within, whether justifiably labelled so or not, that her whole political career had been dedicated to combating. How would it be possible for any of them ever again to speak so knowingly and confidently about the moral superiority of such a totally discredited political system? But instead of taking a triumphant central place in the celebrations, Thatcher remained satisfied with standing sourly on the fringe, an isolated figure, sniping venomously, largely ignored.

As the Eighties were drawing to their dramatic close, both nationally and internationally, I once again found myself being pulled in different, barely connected ways. I was thrilled by the collapse of the GDR and the eventual reunification of Germany that was now inevitable, and shocked by the government's unenthusiastic response to the situation. My regret was not dispelled, though it was pleasantly eased, by Trevor choosing this moment to be in touch once again. Totally unexpected, the same old envelope with the same old postcard obviously inside it was lying on my office desk one bitterly cold winter morning when I arrived at the university. The message read:

DOES IT ALWAYS HAVE TO END LIKE THIS? T.

Although there was still nothing to tell me how he was or what he was doing, it felt warmer than the previous cards, more of a genuine communication. It was clearly a reference back. He was letting me know he now appreciated my earlier gloomy belief that any wholehearted commitment to politics or politicians was bound to end, for an idealist like me at least, in disillusionment. He was also, I supposed, endorsing the solitary condition he had tried to talk me out of in High Holborn. Endorsing it for me, that is, but not necessarily for himself. There was no way he could have known how large a part his words that evening had played in encouraging me for the first time in many years to take an interest in current politics. Or how his postcards had kept my mind alert to the significance of political events that I had little opportunity of discussing with most of my university colleagues.

But although Trevor now appeared to be pointing to some kind of agreement between us, I couldn't believe I had convinced him to change his line at all. Any influence I might have had on him had taken place before we even met. Whatever political doubt he may have been suffering, it would not have been great enough for him to break his party links. They would surely remain the comfort and refuge they had always been, encouraging him to believe that the next time things would be different, convincing him that it was always worth making yet one more effort. It hadn't escaped my attention that his latest message had been in the form of a question. The door was still open, aspirations kept alive, distant possibilities being primed with new hope. There might even have been a resurgence of the belief that politicians should never ever give up and that Trevor's own political ambitions weren't going to be packed away just yet. I like to think that's what it meant.

Whether he had somehow guessed that an expression of sympathy towards me would be especially welcome at this particular moment it's impossible to say, but that's how it felt, and I was grateful for it. I was already beginning to sense that the circumstances of my own life were somehow keyed into public events like the failing Thatcher government and the rusting iron curtain, and now here was Trevor back in touch reinforcing that instinct with his curiously mixed mood of disillusion and new hope. Though it was not this final postcard of Trevor's that brought about the long awaited change for me but a completely fortuitous piece of good fortune.

As the decade drew to a close I was for a while in the happy position of being able to consider my own position from outside the university rather than staggering about on the inside like a stage tumbler being constantly tripped up. Over the past few years I had saved up the academic leave due to me so that when the right moment arrived I could enjoy an uninterrupted final spell of work on my nearly completed manuscript. I was by now entitled to two academic terms off and because in my application I had indicated my willingness to accept as one of them the generally less popular summer term I was granted the heavier spring term as well. When run together with the summer vacation that gave me some nine months to complete my historical web. I had already agreed with the publisher a title for the book. It was to be called *The Haunted Study*, a phrase taken from Henry James's 'The Death of the Lion', one of a number of short stories on the literary life he had written exactly a hundred years earlier in the 1880s and 1890s. Fiercely pessimistic about the future of literary culture and the way its institutions were tending, appalled by the gross philistinism of the age, James's literary artists find themselves torn between the pressures of an uninterested world and their lonely haunted studies, the only places where they can make sense of their lives and the world around them.

A suitable theme for the late Victorians, I thought, and not for them alone. Does it always have to end like this? Yes, of course it does. Phases and cycles, rising and falling. After all, ideals are by their nature unattainable: they are only there as targets to be missed. There are no continuous lines of idealism, not in life there aren't. They're for saints and martyrs, but not for Trevor, not for me. And that feeling was reinforced by the sudden realization that a phase of my own life might also be closed off, that there could be an end nearby to the discontent that had weighed me down for so long. With a bit of planning it looked possible that the temporary spell I was enjoying away from university could be made permanent. I had always assumed that when the moment of escape did arrive it would have to be created by me, the product of my own will, ambition or wishes. But it didn't turn out like that. Instead, a highly acceptable solution was not only presented to me, but pressed urgently upon me by a desperate university administration. No wonder I took so long to see it for what it actually was.

Faced with financial cuts from outside and the need to make savings within, the universities were begging senior academic staff to do the decent thing and take early retirement. The terms on offer were extraordinary. Not only a standard pension, but compensatory years added on, even highly lucrative teaching fellowships for a specified number of years and untrammelled by administrative duties. All sorts of goodies for the early retiree to pack into his or her 'golden suitcase' as the process was coming to be known. The proposals had been drawn up by the UGC. On the verge of abolition and after years of valiant but pointless striving to keep the status of universities unchanged, it had given itself over to negotiating with the government on ways to save money by getting rid of staff on the most generous terms possible. In return, the government was to provide extra money for a number of 'New Blood' posts. The imagery of transfusion was clever, but nonsensical.

Not only was there no observable correspondence between the old blood and the new, between the cost of those arriving and those departing, but in far more important ways the loss was totally disproportionate to any gain. The early retirement scheme could only possibly attract senior members of staff, and among their numbers were to be found the most distinguished, talented, original and productive people in universities throughout Britain. They were the ones in possession of the kinds of scholarly reputations that had traditionally established the worth of individual universities. It was the only true measure. How otherwise was it possible to distinguish one university from another? Yet the universities were now scrabbling around to dispossess themselves of those vital human assets. New blood, in itself, was no answer. Not at least until it had proved the value of its newness by becoming, as it were, what it was replacing. It looked as though the universities were going to prove incapable of helping themselves right through to the end. Or perhaps not. It's difficult to say. The final act was clearly a surrender rather than cooperation. In turning their backs on tradition and agreeing to assess higher education in monetary terms, they were, consciously or not, agreeing that in the future universities would be institutions in which everything was to be priced and valued at unit cost.

I welcomed the accelerated pension terms which in my case would not come into full effect for five years. In the meantime I would be relatively hard up. I also read with grim satisfaction the form letter sent to me which expressed the university's profound gratitude for my past services and thanked me for my generosity in helping the university out in this hour of need. The additional goodies, though, I wanted nothing to do with. They would have kept me connected with the university for a few years longer, and all I could think of was getting away as quickly and as completely as possible. I knew there could be nothing dignified about my departure, and no delay either.

Even so, I was not prepared for the intense relief I felt when the official procedure was over. Nor did I foresee its long-term consequences. I came to feel like Lemuel Gulliver returning home from the land of the Houyhnhnms, though at first our situations appeared to be totally different. Gulliver was full of admiration for the society he had been forced to leave and dreaded rejoining the human race, whereas I was both eager to quit Academia and to return to normality. It should have been easy for me. How could there possibly be a need for me to experience Gulliver's slow, tortuous rehabilitation? But there was. I found that I was now almost as much a stranger as he was to the way of life that I grew up in and had always regarded as normal. All I could do was follow his desperate attempt to be positive and think it 'not altogether out of hopes' that one day a full reconciliation would take place. In spite of my conscious efforts over the previous twenty years to keep myself as unaffected as possible by university ways, it was soon clear to me that I hadn't succeeded. I knew it and so did others. Most academics simply aren't capable of mixing naturally with people who think and behave differently from themselves, and in my experience they are quite happy to stay like that. Keeping apart, only writing for and talking with each other, nurturing an air of superiority is what the intensely specialized training and enclosed institutions of the old-style universities were all about.

For some time I couldn't bear to go anywhere near the university buildings I had inhabited for the past twenty years. Nor could I bring myself to meet or talk with my former colleagues and students. Things weren't so bad that I needed to adopt Gulliver's method of self-protection and 'keep my nose well stopped with rue, lavender, or tobacco leaves,' though strangely enough the realization that such extremes were not for me brought about the most Swiftian insight of all. It was impossible for me to deny that the people I had fled from and had long kept at bay were essentially my natural friends and acquaintances, the people who were most likely to appreciate, understand, and share my own tastes and interests. How could it be otherwise? Hadn't I always known this was the case and still refused to believe it? There could obviously be no turning back, or a wish on my part to do so. I remained cagey, suspicious, still carefully taking detours to avoid the way of life I had once been so keen to enter.

At least the National Library with its miles of books was still independently there, untainted, welcoming and accessible. That at least was a constant, a comfort, a good omen for the future. Using it now in my new liberated condition, it began to feel like starting out in Edinburgh all over again. I had no clear notion of what was to come next, but at least my idealism was intact, even bolstered by the promise of some kind of fresh beginning. Everything was still negotiable, and this time only with myself.